Backwords Forword
My Journey Through Dyslexia

Backwords Forword

My Journey Through Dyslexia

Catherine A Hirschman, MEd

and

R. Christine Melton MD, MS

ISBN 9780615477053

Dedicated to everyone who has ever struggled to learn to read

Contents

Foreword

Where were you, Catherine, when I needed you? If I had been able to lay my hands on this book way back in the sixties when my second daughter, Kate, was at school, I would perhaps have spared her (and me and Enid, her mother) a lot of anguish – and, more importantly, Kate herself.

She was always a robustly cheerful child, happy and popular at the local school in London, but one day, at the age of eight, she came home in tears. We guessed someone had bullied her. True. But we would never have guessed who did the bullying: the teacher.

The teacher was angry with Kate and made her stand on a desk in front of the class while the teacher denounced her for her crime. Which was? Copying words from her diary into her school exercise book. And why was Kate doing that? Because she had trouble spelling and to avoid being rebuked for frequent misspelling she wrote into her diary the correct version of words she commonly misspelled and then copied out these when necessary in the course of an English exercise. She had imagined the teacher would be pleased by the effort, but the teacher implied it was cheating. The teacher had never bothered to find out why Kate went to all this trouble so she humiliated Kate for copying her own writing.

Enid was herself a high school science teacher. She knew Kate was bright. She investigated and suspected Kate might be suffering from a rarely diagnosed condition called dyslexia. Everybody knows about dyslexia now but they didn't then in London. The educational establishment refused to categorize dyslexia as a learning disability. So, Enid helped in setting up the North London Dyslexia Association which lobbied, raised money and started to run summer schools for these children.

Eventually, the British educators conceded that dyslexia was not a sign of stupidity or stubbornness and slowly began to explore treatments.

In this, Britain was catching up with America. The condition was recognized earlier in the US but it is not easy for parents, still less the child, to appreciate that slowness in reading and talking clearly might have a specific cause and that some emotional disturbances may have their root causes in the bafflement and anxiety of dyslexia.

> *emagin how vare hrd it is kop wthe scuksion of*
> *randumlie mangelled wurds.*

My uneducated guess is that this is how some dyslexics would see, 'imagine how hard it is to cope with a succession of randomly mangled words."

Catherine Hirschman had yet to be born when my Kate struggled with her learning disability. All these years later we know so much more now but for all our greater awareness dyslexia may go undetected for years. Catherine, too, suffered growing up despite having the advantage of brilliantly qualified medical parents. She and her mother tell the story of their journey of discovery with an affecting candor but that is not all they do in Backwords Forword. They supplement their own very human narrative with an expert survey of the expertise there now is. This is valuable. A number of dyslexics have been interviewed or written short pieces for magazines, but I don't know of any dyslexic other than Catherine who has written a book that is both an emotional story and a reference source, still less anyone who has married her own perception with that of a parent's.

Daughter and mother bravely embarked on this perilous journey across a sea of shapes and spaces and their success in conveying thought with those pesky words is a public service.

Sir Harold Evans

Harold Evans, former editor of The Sunday Times of London and The Times and in the US president of Random House, is the author two histories of America (The American Century and They Made America, a study of innovation.) He was knighted in 2004 for services to journalism.

He lives in New York with his wife Tina Brown and their two children.

Preface

In the beginning of my final semester of Amherst College, I applied to work as a research assistant in a language-learning lab at the University of Massachusetts, Amherst. A number of my psychology classes from college had touched upon the learning disability dyslexia, and it had sparked my interest to learn more. Part of my job at the language-learning lab would involve administering weekly student assessment tests using a specially designed computer program. On my initial tour of the learning lab, the head of the lab, Professor Royer, explained how the lab worked and about the research behind this method of remediation. After showing me around, he had the lab manager give me the assessment test that I would be giving the students. The test was a series of nonsense words such as; drack, ealtur, and cliel that had to be pronounced out-loud. The test was scored on accuracy and speed and then those numbers were compared to a control group of third graders from around the nation. I scored in the 38th percentile.

Dyslexia is a life-long condition that cannot be "cured." Although it never goes away, there are many strategies dyslexic individuals employ to get past some of the hurdles. This book chronicles, with the help of my family, particularly my mother, my life with dyslexia and some of the things I have learned along the way. As the title suggests, it is first a look backwards at my struggle with words, but then it is a look forward, toward the many things I hope to accomplish, using the knowledge I have gained about how I learn best. The misspelling of backwards and forwards was purposeful. Although I am sure it is irritating to editors, the misspellings highlight that this is most simply a book about words.

Introduction

(Catherine)

I am thirty-two years old. I graduated cum laude from Amherst College with a degree in Fine Arts and Psychology in 2001 and finished a graduate degree, summa cum laude, in Early Childhood Education at Hunter College in 2006. In the spring of 2008, I received a certificate in Conservation Biology from Columbia University. In the fall of 2008, I started a part-time MBA program at NYU's Stern School of Business, which I will complete while I continue to work full-time. I have spent seven of the past eight years teaching at well-regarded private schools in Manhattan while attending classes for various degrees at night. I'm also dyslexic. I wanted to start this book at the end so that the reader knows that despite the many bumps I will recount, that it has all worked out just fine: I love to learn, I continue to pursue higher education and I have found a career that I enjoy. [1]

*   *   *

I am generally very open about myself. As a Student Health Educator in college, I led workshops about things that would make my grandmother blush. I never hesitated to share a similar experience with a friend if it was not a secret and I thought it would help them. However, most of my friends did not know I was dyslexic until I began the journey that has

---

[1] Appendix A gives some basic statistics about dyslexia in the United States

become this book. Looking back, I guess it just did not come up in conversation because I honestly believed that it had been "cured" long ago. I became more curious about dyslexia in college after a few of my Psychology courses briefly mentioned the disorder and its diagnostic criteria. Part of the curiosity stemmed from knowing more about the disorder and realizing that I still experienced difficulty with word retrieval, spelling and organizing my thoughts coherently on paper. While I had become a proficient reader, I still struggled to get through and comprehend the mountains of reading each of my courses required. When I learned about the characteristics of dyslexia, it was as though a light bulb went on in my head and suddenly I understood that my trouble expressing my thoughts on paper was connected to the difficulty I experienced learning to read.

When I realized part way through my journey to learn more about my own dyslexia that honestly talking about my struggles might help others, I knew I needed to write it all down and share it. I sincerely hope that all the setbacks I encountered along the road and continue to encounter can aid others as they journey through their own discoveries of how they learn best. I want this book to speak to parents of struggling children, teachers who work with dyslexic individuals as well as to other dyslexics. My greatest hope is that someone reading this book will realize that they are not alone and that dyslexia is not a roadblock, it is merely a detour, and that it can lead to many unexpectedly wonderful experiences if they are open to them.

I am not a natural writer. I never thought I would even attempt to write a book, so it as surprising to me that I have done this as it is to the people who know how hard I worked to learn to write effectively.

*   *   *

Learning disability experts have written many books about the mechanics of dyslexia and how to work with dyslexic individuals.[2] Some dyslexic individuals have shared brief personal accounts in articles about how they have dealt with their dyslexia. I have always wanted to hear more. I wanted to know how their dyslexia was discovered, how it shaped their lives and what they do to accommodate it today. It is valuable to share individual stories so that researchers and family members can gain a greater understanding of the nature of the disorder. My mother and I felt that it was important to work together to share our story because we can talk about it from many different angles: mother, dyslexic, educator and physician. In an effort to give an even fuller picture, my father, sister and brother have also contributed pieces.

This book is a personal account. I do not endeavor to explain every dyslexic person's individual battle. No two people experience the disorder in the same way. As with any developmental difficulty, I wonder how much of my experience was a result of the disorder and how much was the normal pain of learning and growing. There is no way to be sure. I have compared my experiences with published papers and books written about dyslexia. Most of the experiences I will mention have been supported, if only peripherally, in the literature.[3]

*   *   *

In a family, one child's dyslexia affects everyone. Researchers have found that there is a strong genetic

---

[2] For a working definition of dyslexia, turn to Appendix B

[3] Appendix C lists common difficulties associated with dyslexia.

component to dyslexia; meaning that if a child is diagnosed as dyslexic, there is a very good chance that close family members also have the disorder, even if they have not been formally diagnosed. Secondly, the child with reading difficulties often needs special remediation which requires time, money and planning. There is also an emotional component to dyslexia. As the child struggles, frustration builds and self-esteem takes a hard blow. It is excruciating for parents to witness their child struggle and not know how to assist them. For the grown up family member who might also be dyslexic, diagnosed or not, to see the child struggle is especially difficult because it reminds them of their years of frustration. Dyslexia also affects siblings. When one child in a family of three has the disorder, that child demands more time and help from his/her parents. A very awkward dynamic exists between siblings when one child is an extremely able reader, as my brother was, while the dyslexic child cannot master the most rudimentary reading skills. It is even worse when the younger sibling surpasses the dyslexic's reading ability, as was the case in my family.

*   *   *

For the most part, this book progresses in chronological order. I have tried to inject relevant research where applicable. (Refer to the appendices for more in-depth discussions of specific topics and research findings) I am not an expert in the field of learning disabilities. I have personal experience and have done a significant amount of my own research on dyslexia in and out of academic institutions, but I do not claim to know all there is to know about the disorder. In the past twenty years, there has been an explosion of interest and research in the field. Many studies have been done to determine the exact mechanisms that make the brain susceptible to dyslexia, and what are the most effective means of remediation. I do not attempt to review or cover all of the available research. Instead, I have tried to glean some of the more significant findings and present them in an easy to understand manner. After reading this, if you are interested in learning more about dyslexia, I would suggest looking at the reference list in the back of the book. I have annotated the books I found especially illuminating.

(Christine)

Catherine and I both recently read a book by a famous woman about her personal experience of "dealing" with a daughter with dyslexia. We were both interested in reading it because both Catherine and I have dyslexia, and so little has been written on the subject that is not purely descriptive and clinical. We were looking for personal insights that might clarify some of the confusion that surrounds this subject in general. Would we recognize similarities? Would it yield information, for those attempting to read the book, on how to best cope, and therefore be a manual for other families to look to? Unfortunately, it was a major disappointment for both of us as it ended up being about the thwarted aspirations of the ambitious author, who felt held back by the demands of her desperate child.

We realized that now was the time for Catherine to write her book: the book that describes the inside-looking-out perspective of a person with dyslexia. We also both recognized that she was uniquely qualified to do this. As an extraordinarily gifted young woman who has a Master's degree in Early Childhood Education, she would be able to give the "learning disability" a human context. For obvious reasons, dyslexic people rarely write autobiographical books. Catherine has developed her skills and her confidence over the years and with this has come a love for reading and greater comfort when writing.

Catherine brings to this book a wealth of personal experience. She understands that dyslexia is so much more than just reversing letters. It is sometimes being slow to get the joke, or getting confused about instructions. It is about hitting the wall on a topic when everyone else is charging ahead. It is about anger and frustration. It is about being lonely and sometimes alone with your emotions. The hope is that with her understanding, supported by my own recollections of her formative years, we can put together a book that will help guide parents and children through this confusing and complex disorder. More importantly, we hope to communicate the firm conviction, that it is possible to have a satisfying and productive life doing whatever you desire; given love, understanding and the appropriate tools.

That being said, it is with some trepidation that I undertake this tandem project with my beautiful daughter. Both Catherine and I are very sensitive to criticism and take feedback to heart. This project will no doubt require many revisions and many people will have an opinion. With this in mind, we will forge ahead and I will follow her lead. Catherine is the author and I am her assistant!

Chapter 1

Early Memories

(Catherine)

Most of my earliest memories of my family include either eating meals at the kitchen table, playing ball in the park with my father and older brother David or reading books together. Correction: having people read books to me. While my older brother could read at three years old, I was still struggling at seven to decode words and simultaneously understand what it was I was "reading." Even though I was not reading myself, I enjoyed books with my mother, father or Marina (my "second mother" who lived with us and helped take care of the three kids while my parents worked) each night before bed. I never went to bed without at least one book being read to me. There were the favorites such as "Angelina Ballerina" as well as the George and Martha series. After having dinner and taking a bath, we'd snuggle up together on someone's bed and share a book. The snugglers usually included my younger sister, a grownup and myself. Sometimes David would join us, but more often than not he'd be off reading a chapter book alone in his bed.

Introduction to Parenting

(Christine)

Before I dive into the story of how we figured out Catherine is dyslexic, I thought I should give a little background on our family and my experience as a mother. My first child, David, was born the day before I was to start an intensive internal medicine internship. I took my two weeks vacation for the year and started my internship on July 14th. Between being on call every third night and having a newborn at home, I barely slept. I was very happy and excited to be a new mother and I longed to spend as much time as I could with David, but felt as though there were many forces working against me.

Much of my precious "mommy time" was gleaned in the wee hours of the morning, feeding and attending to an infant who, fortunately for me, was a night owl. I had a constant coffee-fueled headache and felt like a zombie, living in the twilight zone of motherhood. I was not around enough to be aware of all of the nuances of David's early childhood development.

We employed a baby nurse, Margaret, whom we found through a reputable placement agency. She seemed to have everything under control. The baby slept away most of the day and spent the night shift with me. Although I thought this was perhaps a bit unusual, it suited my schedule and David seemed to be doing nicely.

When David was about six months old, a good friend of my husband's, Stanley Greenspan, a renowned child psychiatrist, came for a visit with his daughter, Elizabeth, who was born around the same time as David. Elizabeth was attentive, interactive, rolling over and trying to move forward. It was immediately clear to me that David was behind because he was doing none of those things. Had I been sitting on the park bench observing other children or talking to new mothers, I would have probably made these observations sooner. I approached David's pediatrician and she said that she had also noticed that David was behind on reaching his developmental milestones. The doctor further mentioned that other parents in the neighborhood who had previously employed Margaret had accused her of giving sedatives to their children. Margaret had never formally been charged, but she had been investigated. Why had the doctor not told me either of these things sooner? At this point, I began to seriously question my abilities as a parent. When I got home from the pediatrician's office, I immediately fired Margaret. I also found David a new pediatrician.

We found a new baby nurse, Gerta, for David. Within weeks of Gerta's arrival, David seemed to "wake up" and soon he was on target with all his milestones. This frightening experience made me realize that I needed to be more tuned-in to every single detail of my child's life. I could not automatically trust that the people caring for David were doing everything that was in the best interests of my child.

Catherine's Birth

(Christine)

My life started to feel a little bit calmer when I started my ophthalmology residency. I was only on call every fifth night instead of every third. My husband, Richard, and I thought this would be a good time to have another child because my schedule was better and we wanted to have children close enough in age that they would potentially be friends. We did not spend a great deal of time contemplating whether to have another child because it felt like the right thing to do.

I was very healthy during my pregnancy with Catherine. I did not drink wine and I never smoked. I took no medication, not even a Tylenol. I had no morning sickness, nor anything out of the ordinary to report.

I went into labor with Catherine on her due date. Compared to David's birth, delivering Catherine was extremely easy. It was so quick that the obstetrician, who had been at his mother's house for Easter dinner, did not get to the hospital on time.

Catherine's early development seemed to be totally on target. All the developmental milestones were right on: rolling over, sitting up, walking and talking. Because David was behind his first year, Catherine seemed to be even a little ahead of the game.[4] I was definitely more "tuned in" this time around. Gerta was still working for us and I felt confident leaving her with the children. She was a dedicated and experienced caregiver who seemed to truly enjoy working with children.

Gerta left us when Catherine was a year old and we had the incredible fortune to find Marina. Marina was intelligent, articulate and really got along well with David and Catherine. Marina soon became a second mother to my children and a very important member of our family.

(Marina)

Catherine was a sunny, happy child. She smiled a lot and when we were out together on the street, people would always comment on what a beautiful child she was. Catherine got along well with adults and was always polite. She was very independent and could play happily for hours with dolls and puzzles and make-believe things. We spent a lot of time at the park as well. Each night after dinner we spent time at the dining room table drawing or doing puzzles together. Catherine

---

[4] Appendix D discusses signs of learning differences beginning at birth

was great at drawing and would spend hours drawing these very tiny and detailed illustrations. I would read to the kids if their parents were home late, but usually they were home each night in time to read. David could read, but also liked to be read to. At one point he just started reading to himself because it was never enough, even if we read him "Corduroy" until our eyes crossed. Catherine loved being read to as well, but while her brother radiated towards books, she chose to do other things with her free time like play with dolls, puzzles, or do crafty things.

(Richard)

As a child, Catherine lit up every room she was in and was happy and chatty and beautiful. In every way, she developed beautifully and even at an early age was clearly a gifted athlete. Catherine was also very independent. She seemed to take a great deal of pride in being able to do things on her own. I remember when she was about three years old, she got out of the car, after having been strapped into her car seat by Christine, looked up at us and said very clearly, "I can do it *myself.*" She then got back into the car and buckled herself into her car seat.

Catherine has always liked challenges. Even at a young age, she would pour over puzzles for hours. She also liked it when we gave her practice math problems or when there was a real-life problem that needed solving. Catherine had a very full fantasy life. She loved playing with her dolls. All of her dolls and stuffed toys had names and personalities and they did not always get along. Catherine spent a good deal of time mediating conflicts between Big Martha and Suzie, two of her larger and more charismatic dolls.

Catherine's Eyesight

(Christine)

At three, Catherine's eyes crossed inward. When her eyes crossed, Catherine started to experience double vision. That is when we found out that she has something known as Accommodative Esotropia, which she inherited from me. Catherine is far-sighted and her two eyes have very different prescriptions. It takes a lot of energy for her eyes to converge and focus on an object. For a period, we tried to strengthen the weaker right eye by having her wear a patch over the stronger left eye under her glasses and doing eye muscle strengthening exercises at night. Neither thing seemed to do much, so after a while, she just wore the glasses.

Additionally, Catherine has something in her right eye known as amblyopia. Amblyopia is like having a neutral density filter on her eye. When her right eye is looking at a line of letters on the 20/30 line, she can identify each letter in isolation, but cannot put them together to read them as a whole word. Catherine almost exclusively uses her left eye to see.

When Catherine reads, she accommodates and converges even more than she is already doing which is exhausting for her eyes. Looking back, her trouble focusing on text probably added to her discomfort in reading. Even today, she has a hard time looking at a computer screen for over an hour at a time.[5]

---

[5] Appendix E goes into greater detail about the interaction between vision and dyslexia.

Catherine's Speech

(Christine)

Although David tended to dominate conversations, as a young child, Catherine talked a lot. Catherine could talk for hours and hours. On long car trips, when everyone besides Richard had fallen asleep, Catherine would stay awake chatting away until right before we reached our destination.

When I think back, I remember that although she talked a lot, Catherine did not always make complete sense. I had to listen carefully to get the gist of where she was going with a story. She would be talking about one thing and then all of a sudden, she would be on a tangent about something else.

Catherine had a few articulation errors, such as making the 'w' sound in place of the 'r' sound. She would say "Sawah" for "Sarah" or "weally" for "really." We did not pay much attention to these pronunciation errors because we understood her perfectly. As a child, Richard had also had a few articulation errors and had outgrown them, with some intervention from a speech therapist, by the age of eight. In her Kindergarten Fall conference, Catherine's teachers mentioned her articulation errors and suggested speech therapy. Before we looked into that, we had Catherine's ears tested, to make sure that her hearing was not the problem. Unlike her older brother, Catherine had had few ear infections as a child. As I suspected, from the way she seemed to hear everything Richard and I said, especially if it was not for her ears, the tests showed that Catherine had excellent hearing. Wanting to make sure Catherine wasn't made fun of by her peers and that the articulation errors were corrected, we sent her to Mrs. Duncan, a speech therapist, twice a week.[6]

---

[6] Appendix F discusses early childhood indicators of later reading difficulty, including speech delays, in greater detail.

After about a year of speech therapy, Catherine had mastered the 'r' sound and Mrs. Duncan felt she no longer needed remediation. We were never sure if the pronunciation errors would have worked themselves out on their own over time. Nevertheless, Richard and I were pleased that we had had it checked out and with some help had "licked" the problem.

*   *   *

(Catherine)

The first time I knew something was a little different was when I was taken to see Mrs. Duncan for speech therapy. My brother hadn't gone to see her, so I knew it was something specifically for me, like ballet, only it seemed more serious because it was just the two of us in an office. I had been increasingly aware that I was mispronouncing words because my parents repeatedly asked me to say phrases such as, "red rover, red rover" or say my sister's name. They would say the correct way and have me try to repeat it back. I always tried my best, but I did not really hear the difference between the way I said the word and the way they wanted me to say it. I did not really think that me saying words wrong was such a problem because everyone I spoke to clearly understood what I was saying and most people didn't ask me to repeat myself.

I remember going to see Mrs. Duncan quite clearly. Her office was small and cozy. We played games, she smiled a lot and I got stickers (one of my favorite things) when I did well. She also gave me homework assignments such as practicing certain words and saying rhymes quickly. The memories I have of speech therapy are all positive.

Although I had excellent hearing (my mother always said I had little antennae coming out of my head that caught everything that was going on), I would sometimes have difficulty differentiating sounds. One clear example that I recall is from when I was in Pre-Kindergarten. There was a boy in my class named Patrick and every time the teacher called his name, I would think she was calling my name. I am still not sure why I repeatedly made that mistake because the names are so different and do not even start with the same sound! Even today, I notice that I have trouble differentiating between similar sounds such as the short "a" that makes the "ah" sound and the "o" which to me seems to make the same sound. This difficulty differentiating sounds makes hearing parts of words and learning new languages more challenging, because so much of a language is the subtle differences between sounds.

Teaching David How to Read

(Christine)

I grew up surrounded by books. My father liked to read to us and I always enjoyed children's literature. Starting around the age of two or three, David seemed very curious about reading and wanted to know how to do it himself. I explained to him how to read phonetically and he grasped the concept immediately. Then he read.

From an early age, Catherine enjoyed being read to and was a very good listener. When she was about three, I tried to teach her how to read the same way I had taught David. She didn't seem to catch the drift so I decided to wait, sensing she wasn't quite ready. Around this time, I noticed that when I went to pick up David from Pre-Kindergarten, he would be reading to his friends in the corner, and that he was one of the only ones who could read. Figuring that David was perhaps a bit accelerated, we didn't push Catherine to learn to read, although I wondered why she hadn't picked it up as effortlessly as her brother had.

Chapter 2

Learning to Read

(Catherine)

Starting some time in first grade, I knew something wasn't right. Just as most children can sense when adults around them are anxious, I could tell by the way my parents asked me to read to them that they too thought something was wrong. They were too attentive to every word.

My general recollections of early childhood are understandably a bit hazy now, but some things I remember very clearly. When I attempted to read, I would start at the right place on the page and begin with the first word in the sentence. I would be off to a good start. Sometimes it was the first word and other times it was a few words into the sentence, but as soon as I came upon a word I couldn't recognize, I froze. After the initial fear had abated, I would try to sound out the word as I had been taught. Llll-ahh-uh—guh—huh (laugh). Sounding out words rarely worked because I sounded out each letter in isolation, rarely blending or incorporating known of parts of words. I had no understanding of the patterns of language and how some words were related to other words in how they were spelled or pronounced. I thought of each word as an isolated unit. After failing to figure out the word by sounding it out, I would open my eyes wide, get close to the piece of paper and stare at the word. I figured that if I concentrated hard enough, I would get it. I focused so much on that grouping of letters that I would forget what I had been reading. All my attention was on that one menacing word. Sometimes it would look like another word, so I would guess. My guesses were often outlandish to the point of ridiculous because they were not based in the context of the piece I was "reading." Instead, the guesses usually started with the same letter as the unknown word and might have had a few letters in common, but that was it. Grownups I read with were often confused by how I had come up with such a random out-of-context word and would ask, "Now does that make sense in this sentence?" The harder I tried to figure out the word, the more anxious I became until the page of words became a blur. For a long time I thought that my eyes were playing tricks on me. To clear up the haze that inevitably transcended the page I was trying to read, I would rub my eyes and blink repeatedly. Finally, even though I had lost my place and any clue about what I was reading, I would just keep going because I definitely did not want to start at the beginning again. My reading was so labored, that I became easily exhausted and would want to stop. If an adult read with me, sometimes he/she would give me the word after a few seconds, but that was only partially helpful because I still wouldn't know the word the next time I saw it. Otherwise, he/she would attempt to assist me by saying, "Sound it out." I would want to scream; *"That's exactly what I had been trying to do and it doesn't help!"* Although I tried my hardest, at this point I would feel the tears start to well up behind my eyes. No amount of telling myself not to cry would work and the tears would flow forth.

I do not recall the exact book we were reading, but I have a very clear memory of my father repeating over and over again to slow down and sound out a word. I could hear in his voice that he was getting frustrated because I was not making the right sounds for the letters and I couldn't put all the sounds together to figure it out. I was trying my best to guess the word, so I could move on, but my guesses were obviously not even close. That time, as was the case most times he and tried to read together, ended in me crying and refusing to continue.

It mortified me that I was unable to control my tears. Although I hated crying in front of other people, it was a release. Not only did it ease some of my frustrations, but it also discharged me from having to read anymore. Once I was crying, the adult I had been reading with knew that it was hopeless to go on. I soon learned that it was best to avoid the experience altogether. Luckily, the adults in my life persisted, even though the experience was neither pleasurable nor seemingly rewarding for them.[7]

Richard's Recollections

I was always tentative around the kids when they were younger. Unlike my wife, parenting did not come naturally for me. I had never spent that much time around children until I was a parent. David was an able reader from a young age and we enjoyed reading together at night. When Catherine got old enough, I tried to read with her as well. She was very skilled at memorization. She had memorized whole books so that it appeared that she could read. When we would read a book she did not know together, I would point out words for her as we went along and she would seem to get them, but then, if the word showed up a few pages later, she would have no idea what it was and less of an idea of how to figure it out. The more I tried to get her to sound out words, the angrier she would become. Her whole body would tense up and almost shake. Normally a happy, cheerful child, she would become

---

[7] Appendix G goes over phonemic awareness and how it relates to learning to read.

enraged as I tried to get her to focus on reading the words on the page. When we read together, Catherine inevitably ended up in tears. She would get worked up to the point of being inconsolable. As soon as she started to cry, I wanted to run out of the room as fast as possible. Seeing her so upset and knowing it was something I did, was a terrible feeling. After a number of attempts to read together, she started to push me away, refusing to read with me at all, which, of course, made me feel like a terrible father.

It is my nature to be positive and to expect that all will turn out well with time. Catherine's mood changed when she began to struggle with reading. I readily chalked up her reading difficulties as innate differences in neurological development and was sure that they would work themselves out in time. They did not, and the visible frustration and anger she displayed, particularly towards me, began to really upset me. When you have a child, all you want is for them to be happy and also get loved in return. Every attempt at helping Catherine learn how to read resulted in anger and her pushing me further away, which is exactly the opposite of what you hope for and that set a pattern for later interactions that proved negative and distancing. For a period of time, Catherine wasn't so happy to see me when I came at home at night and would barely speak to me. Catherine began to look at me as some kind of enemy or oppressor because she couldn't get it and I couldn't help her get it and everything I was doing was making her more frustrated and angry. It was an extremely unhappy time for me.

Marina's Recollections

When Catherine was in Kindergarten, it was the first time I thought something was amiss. I saw her continue to write letters and words backwards, even after we showed her the correct way to form the letters. I had seen it in another child, and while I had never spoken about it to the other child or the child's parents, I knew that she'd had problems in school. And although she struggled to keep up in school, she worked very hard and ended up doing very well. Even though Catherine struggled, she kept it to herself for the most part. I could tell Catherine was intelligent and she seemed to be good at everything she tried, especially math. It was just the reading that appeared a little challenging for her. She was more interested in playing sports or doing art.

First Outside Evaluation

(Christine)

In the fall of her First Grade, I began to notice that Catherine was developing nervous behaviors that concerned me such as; grinding her teeth at night, sleepwalking, holding her body rigidly and getting really angry when she was asked to read. I wondered what was going on that was making Catherine so anxious. She never said she was worried or didn't want to go to school, but I could tell something was bothering her. Catherine's teachers were little help. They had consistently told us from pre-K to K to 1st Grade that she was bright, well behaved and above grade level. Her report card from the fall of the first grade was extremely positive. For her learning style, her teacher Ms. Robassa wrote, "Catherine is a highly motivated, eager and involved learner, open to new ideas and concepts." Moreover, for Language Arts she wrote, "Catherine came into 1st grade reading and has continued to seek out new knowledge and skills. She reads above grade level. Catherine has become enthusiastic about writing her own stories." For phonics, all the boxes were checked in the "exceeds expectations" column. Even at the fall conference when we brought up her nervous behaviors, Catherine's teachers still did not think anything was amiss. They even indicated that our expectations for Catherine were unfairly based on David's academic performance and that she was completely on par with her peers.

We were not totally convinced, so we sought out an independent evaluation from a child psychologist at a prominent institution. After he evaluated Catherine (I am not sure what types of tests he did), the psychologist invited us into his office to discuss the results. The psychologist told us that there was absolutely no problem with Catherine, but possibly a problem with our own overbearing expectations for her. We slunk away from this interview embarrassed and chastened. Of course, we later realized that this professional was not just rude but entirely wrong. Parents know their children best and we still knew something was not quite right, but had now been told by two sources that Catherine was developing normally and that our worries were unfounded. So we decided to let it go, although the concerns remained in the back of my head.

Independent Reading

(Catherine)

Independent Reading Time at school never made sense to me. For me it was more like, "Look at the Pictures in a Book and Pretend to be Reading Time." I always picked the books with the most pictures and sat the farthest away from the teachers as possible. There was a spot in my First Grade classroom between the bookcase and the wall that I always tried to get because you could sit and no one could see what you were "reading." Since I couldn't read and was not even interested in trying, I spent my time making up my own stories to go with the pictures. They were elaborate stories about kids going on adventures or animals doing crazy things at the farm when no one else was looking. I learned after a few of these Independent Reading Times that it was important that I turn the page every once in a while and try not to look up too much in case a teacher was watching. If you looked bored, a teacher would call you over to discuss what you were reading or, even worse, want to read with you.

End of First Grade

(Christine)

Around April, the spring of first grade, Catherine became very ill with a staph infection brought on by an infected chicken pox and had to be hospitalized. Because she was so sick, our concerns about her reading development and nervous behaviors were immediately put on the back burner. When she was feeling well enough, we would take her up to the hospital Art Room to do projects, which she seemed to really enjoy. There was also a schoolroom with a teacher to help kids from falling behind on their schoolwork. The teacher worked one on one with the children on workbooks and materials provided by the children's schools. Although she loved the Art Room, Catherine was incredibly resistant to go to the schoolroom, which I thought was unusual because she seemed to love going to her regular school. When I approached the tutor, he thought that since she was above grade level, there was no need to push it. In retrospect, she probably did not like having to work one on one with the teacher on phonics exercises that were really challenging for her. I learned later that one of her coping mechanisms had been to gather clues from her peers as to what she needed to do in her workbooks and how to respond to exercises in class. Without those clues, she was lost and frustrated. Catherine was out of school for nearly two months.

By the time she was back at school, it was time for summer break.

*   *   *

(Catherine)

I first noticed the chicken pox on the day I was supposed to have my seventh birthday party. I wasn't sure what the three little red spots were on my stomach, so I showed my mother, who immediately called off my birthday party. Soon after that I was in the hospital. I do not remember much aside from the beautiful Art Room on the top floor of the hospital. There were lots of windows on the ceiling and it was bright and felt very open. My mother took me there sometimes and we'd do art projects like gluing tiles on the tops of small wooden boxes or making picture frames with popsicle sticks. Art projects always made me feel better. I made things for my siblings and friends because I was a little lonely and missed school. One day my mother suggested I go to the "school room." It was also on the top floor of the hospital, but it was a smaller, darker room off to the side of the art room. There was only one other boy who seemed to be a little bit older than me in the room when I got there. He was working with the teacher, who greeted me and had me sit at my own table. The teacher, a young man with glasses, brought out a few books and asked me to read. I immediately wanted to run from the room back to the sunny art room, back to gluing tiles on boxes with my mother. I do not think I went more than two or three times to the hospital school and each time I disliked it even more. I just did not want to be there. Instead of working with friends, I had to do everything by myself. At school I was always willing to try new challenges, and I do not ever remember refusing to do something a teacher assigned, but I wanted nothing to do with the hospital school.

Writing Samples

(Catherine)

Below are two writing samples from first grade. They are not truly representative of my overall work because one summer when I was home from college, I decided to cull my extensive schoolwork files and only keep my better work. I figured if my children ever went through my things after I had died, I would only want them to find my best work, not the papers that were riddled with spelling and grammatical mistakes in addition to being marked up with unfavorable comments. Unsurprisingly, most of the work that remains in my files is either art or math.

*   *   *

My mother found these letters I wrote to her when I was seven and she was away with my father on vacation. Although it is typical for students at this age to use invented spelling, you can tell I am not hearing the sounds or incorporating spelling patterns by the letters I have chosen to spell some words; such as writing laft for left and palow for pillow.

At this point, I still enjoyed writing and I did not notice that I had a lot of persistent errors. It was not until I started getting back papers with endless red marks that I began to dislike expressing myself on paper.

November 16   1986

Dear   Mom   and Dad
Asof Came over   with
Martha   we went to
Ghacers for lunch, And
Came   home and played
for   3 owers and   than
we   had   diner for 2 owers
we   had   Hot dogs and
totteleny for diner I
codent live the latter
onder the balow Sow
I rot a latter to tell
you a bout my day I
well rit more latter to
yo when   you are
away on a big trip
becuse i mess you very
much.   Sarah is a Pill becuse
she   hid   Davids Rokorder
sow   we went on a
hont   to   find it.
Come   hom   soon
Becuse I mess you
a lot   P.S. I Love
you from Catherine A H

November 19   1986

Dear   Mom and   Dad
I   had   a   wonderfull
becuse   I   got   out   of
bed   in   time   and
tommy   came   on   time
and   gave   us   10   minets to
spar   befor   Park   I   finest
3   work   shits.   I   cot   up
with   Davey   and   at   Park
we   did   2   laps   we   skipt
the   pudels   and   oly   Davey   got
wate   saveing   a   boll   in   clemanashon
and   at   school   we   had
art   we   mad   Manels   I   mad
a   cat   or   a   bear   I'm   not
shor   with   is   the   rit   thing
some   I   thot   it   was
a   bear   becuse   it   looked
more   lick   a   bear   to
me   my   art   tecker said it
looked   like   a   cat.   my he broi
techer   Said   wiy   arnt   your
Parint   here   I   said   becuse   thar
in   itely   the   rest   oy   the   day
she   said   I   was   doing   a   good
job.   Love   from   Cathenine   P.S.   I Lap

My mother encouraged me to keep a diary. We would sit together at night, talk about the day and then I would write an entry. Afterwards, she would look it over for me and help me correct the spelling. I find it interesting that I spelled the word "love" with an "a" instead of an "o" because by the age of five (I was six when I wrote this) a majority of students know how to spell the word automatically.

Second Grade

(Christine)

Although no one else seemed to think there was a problem with Catherine's learning, when she entered Second Grade our antennae were up. There were enough "soft signs" for me to know that something was wrong, even if we did not know what exactly it was. Catherine's report card from the fall of second grade was very positive. For her study skills, Ms. Chorny wrote, "Catherine is a highly focused and motivated student who finishes assignments quickly and moves on to independent work with relish. She is a most enthusiastic learner." For Catherine's general classroom behavior, Ms. Chorny wrote, "It has been rewarding to see her loosen up a bit and enjoy the giggles now and then!" For language arts, which we were still anxious about, Ms. Chorny wrote, "Catherine articulates her ideas with ease. She is an attentive reader who can support her discussion of a book with numerous details drawn from the work. She is an enthusiastic participant in our writing program."

Catherine's spring report card was more telling. For her behavior, Ms. Chorny wrote, "Catherine wrote of herself, 'I used to be serious, but now I'm learning how to have fun.' It is an accurate summation of her year, which saw her participating with less constraint and less concern about being 'perfect'. Due to the fact that she is such an able and fine person, this opening rewarded her with both respect and friendship." For Language Arts: "*Although Catherine did fine work on spelling tests, she did not apply what she learned because she hasn't yet tuned into sound-symbol relationships thoroughly. Reading skills are progressing well even though it is not a favorite pastime.*" This was the first time that a teacher had pinpointed a very specific area of concern. Finally a professional was substantiating what we already knew.

This report card, in addition to the spring parent-teacher conference and our continuing concerns, prompted us to ask the school for Catherine's scores on the Gate-MacGinitie Achievement Tests that she had taken at the end of first grade and the beginning of second grade. The test was the first standardized test Catherine had taken, so we were curious about how she scored in relation to her peers. The principal of the school invited us into her office for a meeting to discuss the results. Tellingly, the school had also invited its lawyer to join in on our discussion. The results of the tests were shocking. She scored in the ninety-third to ninety-ninth percentiles in all areas, except for decoding where she scored in the 26th percentile. The results were a dramatic confirmation that a definable problem existed. The tests highlighted a very irregular profile that I now know is typical of dyslexic students. To Richard and me, it seemed that either no one had looked at the scores, or if they had, had simply chosen not to tell anybody before filing them away. Had I not asked for the scores, Catherine could have continued as she was and maybe not been identified for another year or so, by which point she might have soured on the whole learning process altogether.

Although we could have taken action against the school, we chose to focus our energies on getting Catherine the remediation she clearly needed. The school offered to help in the form of pulling Catherine out of class to go to the resource room, but we had lost our confidence in their ability to help her, so we said that we would take care of this ourselves.

At this point, I took the lead in getting Catherine a full language evaluation. A friend, whose daughter went to school with Catherine, had just had an evaluation of her daughter done. We took Catherine to see the woman they had recommended. After evaluating Catherine, Mrs. F brought us in to discuss the results. She asked Richard and I a number of questions about our own learning styles. She asked us things such as; when you were studying for a test, did you have to write everything out to remember it? Do you have trouble looking things up in an index? Do you feel that it takes you longer to learn new things than it does for other people? Then Mrs. F pointed out that just as Catherine had my eyes, she also had my dyslexia.[8] It was the first time I had heard the word dyslexia used in connection to Catherine's problem or in connection to me. Dyslexia had never come up as a topic in medical school and the only thing I had ever heard about it was that people with it wrote words backwards.[9] Even though Mrs. F diagnosed Catherine as dyslexic, she thought she had a mild case. She proposed meeting a few times to go over some exercises and that that was probably all Catherine needed. Overall, I found Mrs. F to be slightly rude, aggressive and rather unprofessional. I decided to seek another opinion.

*   *   *

I had always known there was something different about the way I learned. But it had been my well-kept secret. I knew it took me longer to learn, that I needed to write everything down multiple times to learn it, that I mixed up numbers when I looked things up in indexes and that certain words I could never spelled right, but I didn't know that other people had similar issues or that it had a name. No one else seemed to notice or particularly care that I learned differently when I was growing up because I did well in school. Furthermore, I don't think my mother would have

---

[8] For a discussion of the link between genetics and dyslexia, turn to Appendix H

[9] Although some dyslexics do write words backwards, it is not one of the main characteristics of the disorder.

even believed me that I thought something was wrong. I had the sense that I had to figure it out myself. I needed to learn how I was going to learn best. I became very motivated to become a reader when in First Grade I realized that knowing how to read gave you access to a whole world of information. I was very curious and I saw being able to read as my key to endless information. As for writing, even though I knew that my written expression was not great, I believed that my ideas were good enough to overcome the composition errors.

After the diagnosis, I searched for literature on dyslexia.[10] At the time of Catherine's diagnosis, there was not lot of literature and what literature there was, was not easy to locate. Mainly, I figured I had done okay without intervention, and that Catherine would do okay as well. I was sure that Catherine would be able to learn and succeed. I never once thought of her as learning disabled, nor did I think that this problem was an enormous obstacle. Rather, I thought of it as a glitch in her wiring that needed some tweaking. Looking back, I realize I did not even explore the issue of my own or Catherine's dyslexia with my family. It did not seem important, although I now see that my younger brother exhibited many similar learning issues; labored reading, difficulty with written expression, and the sense that it takes him longer to learn something new than it does his peers, and is very likely dyslexic. All through his schooling he had been labeled a poor student in most areas except math. He probably would have benefited from knowing my diagnosis and exploring whether he is dyslexic as well. Regardless, today he is a very successful investment advisor.

---

[10] For a discussion on dyslexia and the brain, specifically how the dyslexic brain is different from a "typically developing" brain, turn to Appendix I.

Finding Help for Catherine

(Christine)

We found Mrs. Amron through Richard's tennis partner, who was also a physician. Richard remembered that his wife worked with children who had trouble learning to read and had mentioned to him that Catherine was struggling and that we were looking to find help for her. The tennis partner's wife had worked with Mrs. Amron and recommended her highly. Mrs. Amron was a true professional. Everything about her indicated to us that she knew what she was doing. On our second meeting, she presented us with a very thorough evaluation that highlighted areas where Catherine needed help.[11] Mrs. Amron also offered a clear plan of action. Richard and I felt very confident that she would be able to help Catherine.

Catherine began seeing Mrs. Amron twice a week. I never knew exactly what exercises or strategies she was using, but I felt that she was a professional that I could trust and thus didn't have to micro-manage, which I am apt to do. I also let Mrs. Amron take the lead in reading instruction because I wanted Catherine to do that kind of work with her and not us, so that fixing this "glitch" wouldn't become an issue at home: I didn't want Catherine to have reading help everywhere in her life. I felt very strongly that overcoming this "glitch" should not be the basis of my relationship with Catherine. I think it is a problem when a child becomes an illness, something that has to be "dealt with". Instead, I tried to keep reading pleasurable. I continued to read to Catherine and her sister in the evenings, but never pushed her to read to me. I felt that she would read to me when she was ready.

Catherine became much more relaxed as things moved along with Mrs. Amron. Her teeth grinding subsided and she

---

[11] Appendix J discusses some of the typical components of an assessment

no longer walked in her sleep. Her body even seemed more relaxed. Catherine appeared to understand that reading was not an impossible task and that with Mrs. Amron's help she was going to figure it out. Around the same time, we saw her blossom in other areas. She became more social, probably because she was more relaxed, and continued to develop athletically. Difficulty reading seemed to be less important as her life became fuller.

Chapter 3

Remediation

(Catherine)

In the beginning of third grade, I started seeing Mrs. Amron each Wednesday and Friday for an hour after school. My mother explained that I had a "glitch" when it came to reading and that Mrs. Amron was going to help me fix it. My mother seemed completely confident that together with Mrs. Amron's help, we would resolve this minor issue. My mother also made it clear that I was not going to be seeing Mrs. Amron forever. I was simply getting help to sort out a few small difficulties and that when I had mastered those specific skills, I would no longer need the extra support. Even though I believed her, I still wasn't keen on going. I knew in my heart that I was having some problems and that things were not making sense and that Mrs. Amron was going to help me, but just like any other kid, I would have rather been playing sports or doing a craft project instead of doing even more school work at the end of an already packed day.

I often arrived at Mrs. Amron's apartment for our appointments early, so she would have me sit and wait in her kitchen to have milk and cookies with a nice woman who was often ironing. The woman would give me two Chips Ahoy cookies, but when she was looking the other way, I would sometimes sneak another for good measure.

Mrs. Amron was a tall, slender and slightly austere woman. Her hair was short, brown, and rather poofy. I don't think I ever felt any warmth towards her. Not once did I have the urge to give her a hug or bring her a present. There was something about Mrs. Amron's manner that kept me at arm's length.

Mrs. Amron was all business. As soon as I had put my backpack down, she had me working. Unsurprisingly, she had me read a lot. Sometimes they were real books, but more often she had me read passages in workbooks or on sheets of paper. They usually had a lot of really hard words and I would have to stop a lot to try to figure them out. Reading out-loud made me incredibly tense. As I read, I often encountered words I did not know how to pronounce. In the beginning, I would slyly mumble or make a guess and then move onto the next word just as I did at school and home. However, Mrs. Amron was a savvy woman and quickly caught onto these brilliant tricks. She made me slow down and read in a clear voice. It was painful to hear myself stumble and pause. I wonder if she ever wanted to scream because it was so torturous to have to listen to me.

I remember feeling uncomfortable to the point of being ill when Mrs. Amron would ask me tricky questions about the passages I had read such as, "Why did the main character decide to disobey his mother?" or "Why did Lucy buy the blueberries?" Well, how the hell should I know? I read it aloud to *you*. The problem was that it took so much effort to get the words out of my mouth that I was not able to also think about what the sentences meant, let alone about the deeper, more nuanced aspects of the plot or the intention of the characters. I would try to scan the text for clues after I read a story aloud. In school, it was easier to "fake it" because I could listen to what classmates said and then extrapolate what my passage meant. Rarely did any one student read a whole book or long passage aloud by herself. We always took turns. And during independent reading times it was easy looking engrossed in a book and slowly turning the pages when I thought someone was looking. With Mrs. Amron, there was nobody but me to do the reading and answer the questions. When I got too frustrated, I would try to cleverly (or not so cleverly) change the topic and ask fascinating questions such as, "Where do all of the eraser shreds go when you brush them off of your paper?" Or, "how do they get the ball to stay on the point of a ballpoint pen?" My questions would be followed by her look that meant, "Are you kidding me, Catherine?" After a look, I had to pretend I was genuinely interested and would not be able to continue without a full explanation. A few times we consulted her encyclopedias for definitive answers to fascinating questions such as; how is chalk made? And do squirrels hibernate? However, she made me read the encyclopedic entries, so I soon learned that asking random questions was not going to get me out of reading and I had to try something else. I mean, I didn't really care about squirrels in the least, but having to read all about the squirrel, where they live, what they eat, etc. in an encyclopedia was even more torturous than having to read the passages she chose for me.

My mother always picked me up from the bi-weekly sessions, which was a big treat. I loved having my mother all to myself. Before heading home for dinner, we would go around the corner for ice cream with chocolate syrup dribbled on top. I really looked forward to those times with my mother. We talked about everything except Mrs. Amron. My mother didn't ask me what we did together. Had she asked, I probably couldn't have told her because I soon forgot after the sessions. I'm sure my mother spoke to Mrs. Amron about my progress, but she never did it in front of me. Instead, the two of us talked about school, her practice and the family. Even with the ice cream before dinner and my mother's full attention, I still didn't want to go to Mrs. Amron. It felt unfair. Why did I have to be different? What was wrong with me that needed to be fixed? Was it my fault? Had I not listened well enough at school? Why didn't my brother need special help learning to read? I was also mortified that my classmates might find out that I needed extra help. I almost never told anyone and made the people who knew, mainly my family and one friend at school who also went to a tutor for help, swear they would not tell. No child, especially in middle school, wants to be different from peers. I wanted to be like my friends with their high-top Reebok sneakers and "slap bracelets." I wanted to watch the same TV shows and know what they were talking about when they mentioned a new movie. I also did not want to stick out or be different in any way. I was afraid that people would think I was dumb or that they would make mean jokes about reading backwards. I'm not a person who overly guards my own secrets; I'd rather be open. Having this secret weighed on me at times and I would worry that I would be "caught" and that I would slip up and someone would figure it out and my cover would be blown.

As with many kinds of remediation, while you are going through the process, you cannot see or appreciate the incremental improvements. It was not until much later that I recognized how much Mrs. Amron had helped me.

*   *   *

(Christine)

Catherine's third grade fall report card was the first time that any teacher had mentioned Catherine's academic self-esteem. Ms. Sachs wrote of Catherine's behavior, "Catherine is highly motivated to produce perfect papers in every area, and being a perfectionist is not easy. I think that if we can help her improve her self-image, she would be a happier child. She needs all our support and encouragement." She also wrote for Language Arts in the spring, "Catherine has shown great improvement in language arts. I see her word attack skills are growing and reading is a little easier for her. Her oral reading is a great trial for her, but she does volunteer in class, and I think lots of support and praise will help her." We were pleased that Catherine was in Ms. Sachs's class. We felt that Ms. Sachs really understood Catherine and wanted to support her as she worked through her reading difficulties. We also felt confident in her abilities as a teacher. We had found an ally.[12]

*   *   *

After about eighteen months, Catherine stopped seeing Mrs. Amron. Richard and I were happy with the progress that Catherine had made and only stopped the tutoring because Mrs. Amron, an expert whom we trusted, felt that Catherine was "up to speed." In retrospect, I realize that Catherine could have used a good deal more academic support, especially with her composition skills. I regret, knowing what I do know about her struggles, that we did not have Catherine continue to receive reading and writing remediation.

Fourth and Fifth Grade

(Catherine)

Unlike many of our peers, my brother, sister and I had a good deal of "down time" after school where we could do

---

[12] Appendix K discusses why Third Grade is often times when students are identified

whatever we wanted. As soon as I got home, I would sit down and do my homework. Math homework came first because it was my favorite. I usually finished my work in an hour or so. After that, I could watch informative television shows such as, "Threes Company" and "Who's the Boss?" until dinnertime.

When we were not enticed by television, David and I would be off doing different things. David was usually reading a book. I, on the other hand, never picked up a book to read unless it was for homework. While David poured over "The Chronicles of Narnia" and Gordon Korman books, I was usually working on either a jigsaw puzzle or a craft project. We could both occupy ourselves for hours on end. I went through craft phases. There was the popsicle stick projects phase, the needle pointing glasses cases phase, the making dollhouse furniture phase and the pressing flowers to make stationary phase. There just weren't enough people to make things for.

It was years before I realized the magic of getting lost in a book. I did not really understand why my brother read so much. Reading didn't flow for me, they way it did for my brother. I couldn't decode the words and become immersed in the plot at the same time. However, I loved hearing stories, especially the books on tape my parents played in the car. Being exposed to prose, other than through my own reading, helped to engender a love of literature in me that continues today.

*   *   *

I loved my fourth grade teacher, Mrs. Evans. Mrs. Evans was older, very smart and reminded me of a stern but loving grandmother. She expected a lot from us, and as a result of her expectations, we thrived. I do not know if Mrs. Evans knew I was seeing Mrs. Amron. Teachers talk, so she probably did, but she never referred to it in front of me, nor did she make me feel uncomfortable as though she knew my secret. My clearest memories from that year were the weekly trivia contests. Each cluster of desks would work as a team to answer the weekly questions. All the questions came from work we did during the week. I loved the quizzes because the winning team got stickers or popcorn as a prize.

The theme for fourth grade was heritage. I think a lot of schools focus on families in fourth grade. We each did an extensive family tree project that took many weeks. For one part of the project, we wrote about a special family member, listing some of their attributes accompanied by a portrait of them. I chose to draw and write about my sister, Sarah. I wrote that she was funny, liked to dress up with me and was very sweet. The projects were hung in the hallway. The day after they went up, we were lining up to go somewhere when Jake, a boy I thought was cute, started laughing and pointing at me. A few others joined in. "Your sister is sooo sweaty." I had no idea what they were talking about. It took Robin pointing out that I had misspelled sweet and mistakenly written sweat before I understood. I was so embarrassed. I can still remember my face getting really hot and my body beginning to sweat. I desperately wanted to go into a bathroom stall and stay there forever.

I told my mother about the sweet/sweat incident when she got home. She empathized. The next day, she sent me to school early armed with a bottle of white out and the correct spelling written on a piece of paper to rectify the situation. Had she not suggested fixing the poster, I would most probably have taken the assignment off the wall and hidden it. Luckily once the poster was fixed, no one mentioned the misspelling again. From that point forward, I checked then double-checked anything that was going to be hung on the wall. I also worried more about my work because I realized that I did not even see my mistakes. I knew I needed to find trusted people, mostly my teachers and mother, who could look over my work.

My fall report card from Mrs. Evans was very positive. She wrote for Language Arts, "Catherine's report of her independent reading is always excellent. Her oral presentations are well done and enthusiastically received and she offers fine detail with her descriptions. Her spelling and dictation are outstanding! Her writing is of excellent quality and her ability to organize and create a logical flow of ideas is superb." From this evaluation, one would think that I had a firm grasp of reading and writing. It was about this time that I stopped seeing Mrs. Amron. It must have appeared that everything was right on track.

*   *   *

My fifth grade teacher, Ms. Mennie was uninspiring and utterly disorganized. She was a willowy blond from England whom I liked, but didn't think highly of as a teacher. We did very little work. She would assign the week's homework on Monday and tell us to budget our time so we would finish it by Friday. I usually got it done Monday evening, and I could tell it annoyed her that I had it all done the first night. I especially enjoyed doing all of my math homework as soon as I got home on Monday afternoons. There was something very satisfying about finishing work and getting it out of the way early. It wasn't that I felt pressure to get it done from an outside source nor that I had other extracurricular activities that took up a lot of time. I simply liked getting my work done sooner rather than later. It gave me a certain satisfaction to spend my time, not rush and do the best job I could on an assignment. I think even then I knew that I did better when I had enough time and started assignments early. I felt a lot of pride when I produced work that I thought was correct and well done. I took great care to re-write my math homework on graph paper to make it easy to read and look nice, with the answer neatly boxed (using a ruler of course) so that there would be no confusion. Ms. Mennie would have preferred that I spread it out over the four nights. I think we might have studied Ancient Egypt that year, but I can't be sure. I do not recall any meaningful writing experiences from that year.

The project I remember most from fifth grade was when we made caramel apples. On a Friday in the fall, Ms. Mennie had a chef from our cafeteria come in and work with us. We unwrapped hundreds of caramels, melted them in a huge pot, and then dipped the apples in the warm caramel. We then put the caramel covered apples on a tray covered with wax paper to dry. Ms. Mennie had not done her homework because she did not realize that for the caramel to stick to the apples, the apples had to be refrigerated after they were dipped. Monday morning we found our apples in puddles of caramel. I share this anecdote because it is representative of the entire year. Nothing was very well thought-out. I just floated by. For my spring report card, Ms. Mennie wrote for Language Arts, "She is a keen reader and her comprehension is good. Catherine writes well and her mechanics are excellent." Although I am not sure what she based her evaluation on, this report card again indicated that I was where I needed to be.

Social-Emotional Development

One of the main reasons I chose to undertake writing this book was to bring greater attention to the social-emotional component of dyslexia. Whereas the neurological aspects of the disorder have received a lot of attention in the past four decades, not enough research has focused on the social-emotional side of dyslexia. As children progress, they become more acutely aware of their learning difficulties and this awareness permeates every area of their life. In contrast to the books I have read about a parent's feelings concerning a struggling child, this book attempts to give voice to the dyslexic student.

Dr. Michael Ryan, a psychologist who works with people with learning disabilities and is dyslexic himself, wrote a very good pamphlet for the International Dyslexia Association on some of the social-emotional issues that many dyslexics encounter. Some of the areas include:

- Frustration
- Anxiety (which can lead to avoidance or perfectionism)
- Anger (caused by frustration)
- Low self-esteem
- Depression

There is a high co-morbidity between having a reading disability and having emotional/behavioral issues. It is not entirely clear whether emotional/behavioral issues are a result of having a reading disability or whether the emotional/behavioral problems impede reading acquisition. One theory suggests that the two disorders may share common neurological, genetic, psychological or social risk factors.[13] Regardless of the cause, it is significant that many dyslexics have emotional/behavioral issues. Females appear to be

---

[13] Barbara Maughan and Julia Carroll. Literacy and Mental Disorders. Current Opinion in Psychiatry 2006, 19; 350-354.

particularly prone to anxiety and depression.[14] I believe that for a dyslexic child to reach his/her potential, emotional/behavioral issues must be addressed alongside academic ones.

In the past, I have had several panic attacks and suffered from periods of deep depression. These episodes usually occurred during times of transition. I experience a huge amount of anxiety when I am starting something new be it a job, a course or physically moving to a new home. And though I love art, I have a similar, albeit a much less intense reaction, when I begin to paint. I hate a blank canvas even if I have an idea of what I want to create. Instead of rushing to paint on it, I hesitate to start. I doubt I'll be able to make it look right, even though I have produced a number of paintings that I like, one of which is hanging in my mother's office. The canvas is so overwhelmingly blank that I do not even know where to begin. Most of the time I have to force myself to do a wash on the canvas and start adding in some lines. I do not enjoy the process of painting until I have finalized the composition and there are colors I like on the canvas. At that point, I know where the painting is heading and I have a good idea how I am going to go about crafting it. Only then, can I focus my attention on making it what I want it to be. My favorite part of painting is the last few hours when I am perfecting it. Everything is laid out so I can look closely at each part and play with subtle changes in color. I often find myself reluctant to finish and move on to another blank canvas. I often wonder if this anxiety to start new things is related to my dyslexia. I am initially overwhelmed by thoughts that I might not be able to do, or figure out, something new. Only after I have worked at it for a while do I feel more settled and relaxed. I worked at

---

[14] (Spreen, 1987, Hales, 1994).

reading and I figured it out, but it is that same discomfort thinking I might not figure this new thing out.

*   *   *

Dr. Ryan reports that researchers have found that "when typical learners succeed, they credit their own efforts for their success. When they fail, they tell themselves to try harder. However, when the dyslexic succeeds, he is likely to attribute his success to luck. When he fails, he simply sees himself as stupid."[15] I immediately identified with those words. When I got a good grade, I assumed it had to do with luck, not all the hours spent studying. However, when I did not get a concept, I knew it meant I was dumb and not good enough. Dr. Ryan goes on to point out that feelings of inferiority develop by the age of ten, at which point, it becomes extremely difficult to assist a child in developing a positive self-image. This is yet another reason why early identification of social/behavioral issues and then appropriate remediation is crucial.

*   *   *

Foreign languages and subjects that involved intensive writing were the hardest academic areas for me. I was always hopeful at the beginning of each year that I would do well in all my courses. But slowly, as I got essays returned, I would get a sinking feeling in my stomach. Next came the meetings I would schedule with my teachers to find out how I could do better, followed by the re-writes. In most cases, I was able to do okay, but the times I was not capable of passing the hurdle, I would find myself fading away, trying less hard and paying

---

[15] The International Dyslexia Association Fact Sheet 49.

less attention in class. I did not act out, with a few notable exceptions such as tenth grade Latin, which I will go into in much greater depth later on, in my classes. Instead, I focused inward, feeling shame, humiliation and anger. Anger because studying was not going to make it work. I was angry with my parents who could not help me. I was angry with my siblings for instinctively knowing how to write with seemingly little effort. Sure, my sister worked hard, but it was without the constant frustrations. She did all her work, but she also got to bed early. I was up well past midnight most nights and even then I only went to bed out of sheer exhaustion, not because I ever felt as though I was really finished.

I also felt a great deal of loneliness. I never wanted to admit to friends how hard I had to work for my grades. I particularly hated when other girls would ask how I did on a test. Sure, it felt good to say a good grade, but the flipside was when I did not do well, I did not want someone expecting me to tell her because I had told her another grade at an earlier time. Also, if I lied, they might ask to look at what I had put down for an answer on a question they had missed. As a result, I actively avoided discussing my grades with my classmates, though this kind of comparison was inevitable.

*   *   *

Many students with dyslexia struggle so much that at a certain point they give up. It just is not worth it to work so hard all the time and still not achieve. I probably would have given up and resigned myself to failure had I not had such a wonderful support system that loved and encouraged me. In addition to my parents, I had Marina, who is a second mother, cheering me on. She had an unwavering faith in my abilities and praised me for my hard work. I never understood it, but she has always thought that I could do anything I set my mind to. She celebrated my achievements and reminded me of them often. If I were upset about a recent grade, she would point out that I had done well on another test last week. I rarely shared my grades with anyone, but I usually told Marina, minus a few of the bad ones.

Just as importantly, I had things, other than academics, that I was good at doing. Things I could do better than my siblings could. I was good at sports. Although it caused tension when we were children, I was better at sports than my brother was. Sure David was an amazing writer and artist, but I could beat him swimming or running. I felt really good about my athletic accomplishments because when we were compared in this domain (which was not often because we were interested in such different things), I came out ahead.

Art was another outlet for me. I have always loved craft projects, especially when I am making a gift for someone else. When I was twelve, I started a small jewelry business. I made earrings, bracelets and necklaces, which I sold at local arts and craft fairs. I came up with the idea for the business because my mother could not possibly wear all the necklaces I was making her. My mother suggested getting cards printed that said "Jewelry by Catherine." The funny part was that neither of us could figure out the correct way to spell jewelry and the printer obviously hadn't checked the spelling, therefore, we had to have the cards reprinted twice. One summer I built a dollhouse from a kit, and gave it to family friends. I also sewed a quilt for my bed over a long winter. I was and still am never without a craft project.

Volunteering has been and will always be an important part of my life as well. When I was younger, I would hang around after school to help my teachers tidy up. I loved when they asked me to help a peer with math or science homework. Helping other people has always been a hugely rewarding activity for me. I probably glean more personal satisfaction from the act of helping than the person gets in assistance. I have never pretended that volunteering for me is a fully altruistic act. I completely recognize that I get back as much as I give. Today, I regularly volunteer on a variety of projects including mural painting and tutoring low-income students for the SATs.

Dr. Ryan wrote; "Many successful dyslexic adults deal with their own pain by reaching out to others. They may do volunteer work for charities or churches, or choose vocations that require empathy and a social conscience. These experiences help dyslexics feel more positive about themselves and deal more effectively with their pain and frustration."[16] I completely agree. Volunteering meant I could focus on other people and "fixing" or at least lessoning their problems. I do not think it is an accident that I have chosen the field of education. I have always loved helping other people, and I wanted to work in a job where I felt I was contributing to a greater good. Jobs where I sat in front of a computer, isolated from other people and removed from my goal of making a positive impact on the world never lasted long. I would find myself dragging my feet to work, daydreaming, and generally unsettled. Sure, I was qualified for these jobs and some of my strengths, such as organization, strong critical thinking and attention to detail were well suited to the jobs, but there was just something missing. I came to the realization after one such job, that for me to sleep well at night, I had to feel that I was making the world a better place, even if it was imperceptible on a given day.

---

[16] The International Dyslexia Association Fact Sheet 49.

Sixth Grade

(Catherine)

In sixth grade, my parents decided they wanted me to switch schools. In New York City there is a test commonly referred to as the ERB (Education Review Board) that assesses skill levels in various domains. In order to apply to private schools, an applicant has to take a chronologically appropriate ERB test. Although my report cards had improved and I seemed to be reading fine, my parents thought I should see Mrs. Amron again to prepare for the test. I was much more hesitant. Just like in Third Grade, I knew I could use some help, but this time around I was a lot less comfortable admitting that I still had trouble reading and comprehending at the same time.

This time around, the routine was different. Now if I arrived early for an appointment, there were no cookies (had she caught on to my generous allotment schemes?) nor milk. Instead, I waited alone in her sitting room, where I was supposed to do homework or something. Since I could only do my homework seated at a nice large table and no good worktable was available, I mostly just snooped around the room. She had some nice paintings and a few pictures in frames scattered about the room. I particularly liked her collection of coffee table books. On the window ledge, there were a few green houseplants. At first, I just looked closely at the plants. Then I found myself rubbing their leaves between my fingers to see if they were real. They were. Then one day, I noticed that the soil had these tiny white balls in it, which were probably some type of fertilizer. When squished between my thumb and forefinger, these fertilizer balls made an oddly satisfying crumbling noise. The ball squishing turned into digging, squishing and then spreading the remains on the rug somewhere. This quickly escalated into me semi-killing the plants. Not surprisingly, it wasn't long before I was caught. Mrs. Amron confronted me one session. She pointed out that she had noticed a pattern of soil accumulating on her rug on days when I worked with her. I had nothing to say, it was clear I did it and I am not much of a liar.

After our session that day, she had my mother come up for "a talk". I almost died of embarrassment. I was usually so concerned about doing the right thing that I rarely got in trouble at school. To be honest, I'm not totally sure why I dug out, squished then spread the fertilizer balls on Mrs. Amron's sitting room rug. I had not thought to myself, "I am mad about having to come here", but it seems obvious now that that had something to do with it. When interrogated, I gave the lame excuse that I did not like having to come to her house because it meant I had to miss hanging out with my friends. I was not thinking that this might be a good way for her to stop working with me, although in retrospect I was probably hoping for that outcome. Having to go each week was a reminder that I was still having some trouble and that made me uncomfortable. Just as in Third Grade, I kept it a secret, but it was even harder this time. Friends would ask to hang out and I would have to make up excuses for why certain days didn't work. And it honestly just felt satisfying to crush those little white balls. They made a little popping sound as they were crushed and then I would roll my fingers in a circular motion until all that was left was dust.

Years later I contacted Mrs. Amron. At that time, I was almost finished with college and thinking about working with dyslexic children. I hoped by then she had forgotten about the plant-killing incident, because I was, and still am shameful about it. We set up a lunch date to talk. Walking into her apartment, I was immediately transported back to middle school and the feelings of extreme discomfort. I wasn't sure what to do with myself, or where to put my hands. I just stood there until she told me what to do, just as I had done in Middle School. Everything in her office smelled and looked as I remembered it. Her office was exactly as I remembered it. She even had the same green felt-covered pencil case with the face on it that I remembered staring at when I did not know some answer ten plus years earlier. She still had not replaced the over-burdened bookshelf over the desk that looked as though it might collapse at any given moment. I wonder how many uncomfortable students had sat at that desk in the orange plastic chair with her over the years. How many of them had become aware of her slightly crooked teeth? How many had been astute enough to notice the small yellowish build-up of plaque between her front teeth?

One of the reasons I had contacted her was that I was curious to know about what we had worked on together and how she had approached my deficiencies. However, as luck would have it, Mrs. Amron had recently cleaned out her files and my records had been sent the to circular file. She could not tell me why or how she had decided that I was "finished" and no longer needed help. What I have learned through experience and research is that although a person with dyslexia may develop successful coping strategies, they are never "cured". One of my biggest wishes today, is that I could have gotten help learning how to write whether or not it was under Mrs. Amron's tutelage. Writing was an area that I really struggled with through college. I am not a confident writer, but I continue to work on it and probably always will. Mrs. Amron dismissed the question whether I needed more help than I got, but I really wonder about it. I wondered whether her dismissing my question was because she regretted not helping me more or if she thought I was just being dramatic. Maybe, if I had really worked on my writing with some specific help, I would have been able to bypass some of the frustration and self-doubt that has accompanied nearly every written piece of work I have ever handed in. There was a part of me that was a little angry that Mrs. Amron had not seen that I needed help writing or had suggested to my parents someone else that could help. How had she not seen the link between reading difficulties and writing? She *was* the expert. Why had she dismissed me without at least alerting my parents that they should be aware going forward that I might need some support with my writing? Then I remembered that at the time, people did not know as much about dyslexia and maybe she really hadn't thought it was part of her job to look at writing, because she had been trained to look primarily at reading.

Chapter 4

Switching Schools

"(Catherine)

My ERB scores came back and I had done fine in the reading comprehension subtest. The score was not consistent with the other subtests, but it also was not a glaring anomaly either. Moreover, since the score was good, I think we all assumed that the dyslexia stuff was finished. Furthermore, I got into all the schools my parents had applied. I had even gained entrance into Hunter College High School, which is a New York City Public School for Gifted and Talented students. Admission is determined based on scores from a single standardized test. Interestingly, of the sixty odd students at my old school, the only people who had qualified to take the entrance exam and than were admitted to Hunter were David I., myself, and a friend who was also dyslexic. I really wanted to go to Hunter. I knew it was a good school and, as opposed to the other choices, which were private schools, it was free. Although I am sure my parents thought about the cost even more than I did, they decided that they wanted me at a smaller school where I could get more individual attention. They felt I could really excel in a more intimate environment. The private schools also had a lot of sports teams and art offerings, which they knew I enjoyed. After ruling out Hunter, my parents let me choose where I wanted to go, so I chose Chapin. I chose it because I had liked the girls and felt comfortable when I visited.

*   *   *

(Christine)

When Catherine started Chapin, we did not alert the administration about her past reading issues. We thought we had "solved" the problem with the help of Mrs. Amron, and we wanted to see how Catherine would fare. We were confident that Catherine was a capable girl and that she would rise to the new expectations. We weren't sure that it would help her if we told all of her teachers ahead of time that she had had trouble learning to read. It was really the "wait and see" approach.

*   *   *

(Catherine)

A lot changed when I began seventh grade. For starters, there were only girls in my classes and I had to wear the same puke-green skirt every day (luckily that skirt has since been phased out). More importantly, my teachers' expectations of my work were much higher than they had been at my old school. My new classmates had been learning how to write essays for at least two years.

Seventh grade English did not go as well as I hoped. One of the problems was that I was coming from a school that had not worked explicitly on grammar and writing, but it was assumed that I had certain writing skills, which I did not possess. My old school was considered very progressive. Instead of the "drill and kill" approach to phonics and grammar, their philosophy was that I would learn everything I needed to know in the context of reading and writing. While that philosophy clearly worked well for my brother, it did not seem to take with me. My seventh grade English teacher wrote for the fall semester: "Catherine would benefit from continuing to work on her written expression so that she can express more complex ideas without making many syntactical mistakes." Another problem that surfaced that would continue to plague me all the way through college: organization in my writing. Although my life was very organized, I had no idea how to effectively organize and coherently express my ideas on paper. When I say I was organized, I mean I was the definition of organized to the point of being slightly obsessive about having everything in its place. At the beginning of the year, I assigned each of my classes a color that matched the colors in my weekly schedule. Math was blue (my favorite color), English was red, Science was green, etc. Every piece of paper associated with that class, whether it was the syllabus or an assignment, was placed chronologically in the proper binder. As soon as I received an assignment, I three hole punched it and then I put it in the right folder or binder so I was sure not to lose it. My weekly planner was clean and orderly and all of my assignments were written in and crossed out upon completion. I even had a handy dandy label maker to label the folders and binders. How could a person so compulsively organized not be able to order her thoughts onto paper? I knew that if I kept up with my work in a logical fashion, I had the best chance of doing well. I have read that many dyslexics have trouble organizing their schoolwork. They are constantly losing assignments or misplacing notes. I had the flip side: I was rigidly organized.

I spoke in full sentences that had main points and logically progressed. I could discuss issues in a meaningful way. But frustratingly, when it came to expressing myself on paper, it was as though my thoughts became jumbled on the way from my mind to my hand. I created sentences on paper that I would never have said aloud and horrified me when other people read aloud to me. Interestingly, when I reread my work, it usually sounded different then when other people read it to me. I am pretty sure I moved words around in my head as I reread what I had written, making editing almost impossible.

I went to Mr. Chapman, my English teacher, for help. I explained that I did not understand where to place commas, how to fix run-on sentences or what to put in the different paragraphs of an essay. I pointed out that we had not been taught those things in my old school and if we had, I must have missed that day. He referred me to a book on grammar and said to memorize the rules. I faithfully wrote down what nouns, adjectives and verbs were and how to use them. I wrote down the rules of commas and semi-colons on flashcards. I memorized the definitions. I could tell anyone the definition of the terms, but I was not able to effectively apply what I had "learned" in any kind of meaningful way. I blamed my old school for not teaching me how to write, but it was more than that. What I did not know at the time and did not realize for many years was that my difficulty with writing had a lot to do with my difficulty in learning to read.

Writing quickly became an area of great anxiety for me. I knew as I wrote that it was not quite right, but I had no idea how to fix it. Part of the problem was that when I read my work out-loud to myself, I was not able to hear the mistakes, because I would switch words around, not realizing that what I wrote was not what I was reading back to myself. Strangely, it was as though I read what I wanted to see, not what was really written. I interpreted the code of letters to my liking. I did it when I read books as well. I would think I saw a word that was not there or I would switch words around. It took me a long time to learn how to read only what was written and in the order it was written. Even today, I sometimes stop myself while reading because I have added in a word that makes no sense. While I am reading, I constantly check my comprehension and whether what I am reading makes sense. I think Mr. Chapman thought I was not applying myself.

As my frustration in English continued, I found myself daydreaming and passing notes in class. I moved from my front row seat to the back corner of the small classroom. From the back row, I made fun of Mr. Chapman's long highlighted hair and the way he tossed his head to get it out of his face. One time I was even sent from the room for being disruptive! I had never been reprimanded in my old school or in any of my other classes. The most maddening part of it all was that I truly wanted to grasp what I was being taught, but I simply didn't understand why some sentences were fragments and others needed semi-colons. Commas eluded me completely, and the passive voice seemed to be the only one I knew how to use.

*   *   *

My first year at Chapin, I also struggled with History. I loved the teacher, enjoyed the subject and the discussions, but did not do well on the tests. On tests, I was solid on the multiple-choice questions, but really struggled with composing the essays and short answers. I studied hard and knew all of the information, but I had not the slightest clue how to organize my responses in such a short amount of time. Mrs. Chapin (yes, she had the same name as the school) took me aside after one test and said she knew I understood the information and could tell I had studied hard, but that my writing was confusing and unclear and that was why my grade was lower than it might have been. On the one hand, I was pleased that she knew I had worked hard and knew the information, but on the other hand completely frustrated that I did not know how to make my writing clearer and more concise. The theme of knowing the information, but getting points taken off for poor writing ability played out repeatedly in high school and in college. I could almost predict that when I received a graded paper back that one of the comments would mention that points had been taken off because of my writing. I even remember getting a paper in college with the grade A/B-. The A was for content and the B- was for the writing. A B+ overall is a fine grade, but it was so upsetting to know that I had an A for content and it was my writing that lowered the grade.

Difficulty writing and organizing thoughts is a common characteristic of dyslexia. Although dyslexics are of average or high intelligence, effectively writing down ideas is a struggle. So many of the programs I have researched focus all their attention on the mechanics of reading and neglect to address writing. It fits that a person who is a better reader will probably be a better writer, but that equation is lopsided in dyslexia. Yes, I could read better after some assistance, but I still could not form grammatically correct sentences. My brother once said that he knew how to write well from reading so much. He said he learned how to make good sentences and use punctuation from authors. It makes sense that the more you read, the better idea you have of what is good writing. Although I was reading more, the grammar behind what I read did not translate into a better understanding of how to effectively write. Each time I sat down to write, it felt as if I was starting fresh with no clues.

*   *   *

Either the girls at my new school were very polite or they did not notice that I struggled, because they never teased me when I had trouble reading out-loud. Most of my frustration came out when I was alone in my bedroom at home. Behind the closed door, I labored over my assignments. Tears would flow when I couldn't understand how to do something. My parents helped me when I asked, but I found it incredibly stressful to work with them, especially my father. My father would mark up my papers beyond recognition--to the point where I just wanted to give up. He would get frustrated at me and say he was just trying to help. I knew that, but it was not the kind of help I wanted. He would say, "Don't you want to hand in a good paper?" Of course I did! I wanted that more than anything else in the world, but getting back papers marked up beyond recognition was overwhelming and defeating. I probably would have never asked for help, except that I knew I needed it, especially with my writing. It was an equation I weighed in my head: try to do it myself and getting incredibly frustrated and upset or ask for help and getting upset and frustrated. Neither way worked all that well.

I found teachers to be the best help when it came to homework, but I was embarrassed to ask for help too often. They would want me to bring a draft of what I had done so far to discuss it. Although it was a seemingly reasonable request, by the time I had a draft, I was ready to be done with the paper. What I needed was help organizing what I wanted to say in addition to how to go about writing it. Once it was on paper, they would focus on grammatical and spelling errors, but not address the problem that I was not able to apply what I had learned when composing a new paper. I wish I could have received more targeted writing instruction.

Foreign Languages

(Catherine)

I had considerable trouble with French my first year at Chapin. The other girls had already taken a year or two of French by the seventh grade. In order to catch up, the summer before I started Chapin, I started "learning" French. On our family road-trip to Eastern Canada we listened to French language learning tapes, suggested by my father's best friend who was a language genius and was constantly picking up new languages this way. We started playing the tapes on the ten-hour trip from New York to Montreal. Although it was repetitive, it was difficult for me to correctly imitate the new words I heard or to remember them, much less use them in any meaningful way. We all soon wearied of the experience and switched to listening to novels on tape. I think my siblings might have gleaned more from the tapes than I did.

When we returned from our two-week family odyssey, I began private French lessons. In the beginning it went well, but as soon as we moved pass, "Como tallez vous?" I got very confused. Luckily, I was working one on one with a tutor who was able to repeat phrases for me until I understood them.

I can recall that most of the time I spent in French class at Chapin, I had the sense that I was missing some vital piece of information. It was as though I had been in the bathroom when the teacher gave away the answers to the quiz. I was always on the right page in my book, but I never quite knew what was going on. I took copious notes, but that was not particularly helpful because I did not know how to spell and could not hear what the words were anyway. My notes were a ridiculously jumbled attempt to organize the chaos. Memorizing from the book was more helpful because I could visualize charts and pictures. Reading out-loud and responding to questions was the worst. I disliked reading out-loud immensely. My reading was painfully slow, my accent was horrible and I never understood what I read. It must have been excruciating for my French teacher to hear the words ever so slowly butchered. When it was my turn to answer an aural question, I would try to give the simplest possible answer. This annoyed the teacher because she understandably wanted us to practice our vocabulary, not just use oui or non. My written assignments were similarly terse. I stuck to one type of sentence structure. I did not understand how to vary the sentence structure and still have it be correct. Whenever I attempted to vary the sentence structures, it had even more wrong with it than my simple sentences. I remember getting back papers with many corrections that I did not understand. The corrections often concerned exceptions to rules or stylistic choices. Instead of incorporating those corrections into my next assignment, which I had no clue how to do, I simply made the same mistakes again and again.

*   *   *

Although it seems obvious that a student who has trouble learning their native language may also experience difficulties acquiring a foreign language, there has been very little research done on the topic. In the face of a new law that all Scottish children must learn a second modern European language, Crombie (1997) decided to investigate the impact of this new law on those children who struggle(d) with learning to read English. Unsurprisingly, she found that there were significant differences between the age- and experience-matched controls and dyslexic children in their achievement in the four domains of foreign language acquisition: reading, writing, listening and speaking. She also noted that:

"It appears likely, however, that the degree of difficulties which pupils have in learning a foreign language is related both to the degree of difficulties they have had in learning their own language, and also... (The level) the pupils are currently at in dealing with their own language."[17]

More simply, students who had a hard time learning to read and write in English will most likely have a similarly hard time learning a new language. More importantly, the degree to which the student received help in their native language directly affects which tools they use to learn a new language. However, even a student who has received a great deal of intervention in English and has "come to a stage where reading and writing skills [are] reasonably acceptable to teachers, [the] underlying phonological processing problems may still affect the learning of another language." [18] Some of the core deficits associated with dyslexia: weakness is phonological processing, poor working memory, syntax confusion, poor auditory discrimination and faulty auditory sequencing may prove insurmountable obstacles to the acquisition of a new language. Crombie recommends that all children study a foreign language initially. At the very least, she argues, the study of a foreign language will expose children to the flavor of a language and the culture of another country. Crombie also suggests ways to approach teaching dyslexic students a foreign language; teach the students in small groups, only present small chunks of information at a time, incorporate a multi-sensory approach and allow greater processing time for

---

[17] Margaret Crombie (1997) The Effects of Specific Learning Difficulties (Dyslexia) on the Learning of a Foreign Language in School. *Dyslexia* Vol. 3, pg. 39.

[18] Ibid 40.

students. Even with these accommodations, some students will not be able to cope (as determined by teachers, parents and educational psychologists) and alternatives will need to be found. Because "if otherwise able children are compelled to persist in learning a subject in which they consistently fail then they are liable to become de-motivated, and emotional and behavioral problems may result."[19] It is much more beneficial for everyone involved to acknowledge whether learning a second is language is feasible for a student, than if the teacher, student and the students' parents all continue to bang their heads against the wall.

Although it is likely that a student with dyslexia will have difficulties acquiring a foreign language, it is by no means impossible. Charlann S. Simon, a dyslexic individual, documented her quest to master the French language. Although she repeatedly found herself up against difficulties such as the inability to fluently retrieve basic structures or to speak in full sentences, she persisted because of her love of the language. After seven years of study, she continues to take entry-level courses. Simon writes that some of her persistent problems include; difficulty making sound/symbol connections, remembering and applying grammar and spelling rules, and drawing on phonological working memory to repeat back words and phrases.[20]

Simon goes on to suggest strategies for learning a foreign language. The first thing she suggests is to plan carefully to allot up to three times as much studying time as intellectual peers are doing. She also suggests working with an instructor who not only uses visual displays, but also is willing to use English for clarification of grammatical principles. She also

---

[19] Ibid 29.

[20] Charlann S. Simon. (2000) Dyslexia and Learning a Foreign Language: A Person Experience. Annals of Dyslexia. Vol. 50 pp 155-187.

recommends making course content as personally meaningful as possible.

Simon goes on to address language instructors with suggestions of how to reach their dyslexic students. Those suggestions include; teach how to learn what is being taught, provide multi-sensory support, provide incentives to speak the foreign language in class, develop compensatory grading procedures that encourage dyslexic students to remain in challenging courses, and make learning a foreign language an attainable goal.[21]

Catherine at Chapin

(Christine)

The transition to Chapin was not easy for Catherine. Many of the girls had been in school together for seven years and cliques had already formed. Catherine managed the social aspects very well, but the new academic demands posed a greater challenge. Catherine's switch to Chapin made it clear to Richard and me how inadequate her old school had been in teaching writing skills. From what I could tell, her old school had never required them to even compose a simple structured essay. Within Catherine's first month at Chapin, it was obvious that Chapin was a much higher caliber school than the one she had previously attended.

Catherine did not complain about the new academic expectations. We could see that she was stressed, but she never said, "I can't do this." In retrospect, we should have intervened and gotten her some support. It was really a double whammy for her: she was poorly prepared and dyslexic. Had we known to get her more academic support, it would have probably

---

[21] Ibid 184

saved her a good deal of grief. Fortunately, Chapin had small classes and Catherine seemed to grasp new concepts easily and was not way off from where she should be in most subject areas.

Aside from the challenging academic transition, we were gratified with our decision to switch Catherine to Chapin. She seemed to really enjoy her courses, all the clubs and sports teams as well as her new friends.

Here is a letter she wrote about the transition to Chapin and the new expectations as well as a cartoon. Both she left on my pillow one night.

Dear Mom & Dad,

It has come to my attention that my life is rapidly changing this year. 1. Much more homework. 2. Less time to spend with you and everyone. 3 much harder work.

First I would like to thank you for your help and patience. It has been quite a surprise to me.

I'd also say that I really appriciate taking me to San Fransico, It is something to look forward to and have a wonderful time.

Inside I fell wierd, because I usto alway have time to space and time to goof-off. Now every minute can be used studying spelling etc. I also know It is

not hard as it is
going to get.
I'd like to thank
you again for everything.
love

Catherine
H.

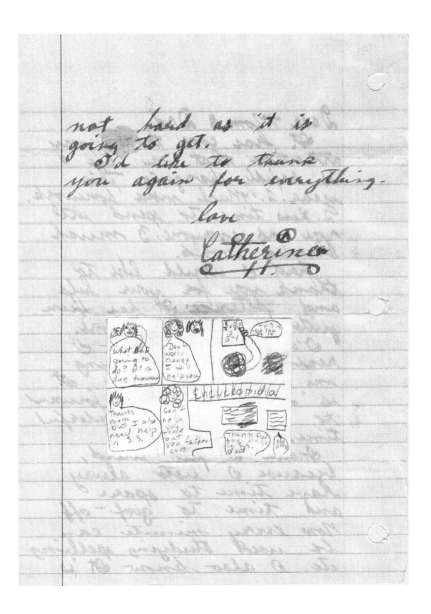

Cheating

(Catherine)

It is tempting to cheat on schoolwork, especially when you do not understand it. There were times I thought about copying a friend's answers or reusing an essay my brother had written. Doing that would have provided a quick fix and circumvented some of the anxiety and frustration that went along with me doing the work myself. But, even at a young age, I knew that cheating was an incomplete fantasy. Sure, that assignment might be right, but I wouldn't know what I needed to know. And then, when the next assignment or test came, I *really* wouldn't know what to do.

Although it was painful to get poor grades, I knew it was better to do that then to cheat myself out of knowing. I have always genuinely loved learning. I enjoy gaining knowledge and applying it to new problems. I reap satisfaction from really understanding concepts. Had I cheated, I would have stripped away my remaining academic self-confidence. Cheating would have made me believe that I was incapable of doing my schoolwork by myself. Although I did not always receive the marks I desired, I am proud of my efforts and of my achievements.

Siblings

It is hard not to compare yourself with your siblings when you grow up in the same household and have the same biological parents. My brother David, who is two years my elder, earned the highest marks, while never appearing to do any homework. Sure, he was always reading, but I have very few memories of him hunched over a textbook studying or reviewing flashcards. Maybe it was because I spent so much time alone studying in my room with the door closed, that I missed the opportunity to see him work. On the other hand, David tended to stay awake later than I did, so maybe that is when he did his work. Nevertheless, it seemed that instead of doing his homework, David preferred to find inventive ways to distract me from doing mine. Sometimes he made strange noises outside of my door, other times he would come into my room and lie on the floor moaning, and my favorite was when he'd pretend to need my help with something only to find out he just wanted to pull me away from my work.

Some days David would leave early for school intending to write an essay, that was due that day, in a coffee shop along the way. And of course, he would usually earn an A for all of the time and effort he had put in. I hated him for that: both the ease with which writing came to him and his cockiness. I would start assignments way in advance and toil away at them sometimes late into the night, but no matter how hard I worked, I never got an A on a written assignment unless I rewrote it with the teacher's help.

I know my brother knew I struggled with reading and writing. It would have been hard to have missed all of my frustrated tears. Barely a year ago, we were talking about a facet of global climate change and I referenced a few books I had read on the subject. He looked at me stunned (although he later claimed he was merely joking, which of course I didn't find funny) and said, "I didn't know you read." Here I had finished college and was close to completely my masters in education, but he still thought I did not read. He had rarely observed me with a book while we were growing up and, just as I still believe writing comes effortlessly for him, he still thinks I do not read for pleasure.

*   *   *

My younger sister, Sarah, was extremely funny as a child. She could imitate almost anyone. Like our older brother, Sarah was an early reader. Reading came easily for her and she enjoyed it. Although four years my junior, she was reading at a similar level when I was in third grade and she was in kindergarten. She never flaunted her prowess or tried to show me up. It would have been very difficult for me had I realized at the time what an able reader she was. Instead of showing me up, she was forever agreeing to be my pupil in the classroom we had set up in the basement. Because I only ever taught her math, she was doing multiplication and long divisions before any of her friends.

Sarah was jealous of my weekly visits to Mrs. Amron. I don't think she really knew why I went, but she knew she wanted to go as well and was not allowed. Her jealousy made going for remediation feel just a little bit special.

*   *   *

Both my brother and sister appear to pick up foreign languages with ease. My brother took Latin throughout high school and got a high score on the Latin Advanced Placement test. In Lower School, my sister did well in French and even took some Japanese. In college she took a few French courses as well as German and spent a summer abroad living in Berlin. My father is also adept at languages. He endlessly impresses foreigners with a sentence, some more appropriate than others, in their native tongue.

When report cards were sent home, my parents would give my brother a "talking to" if he hadn't earned all A's. David didn't seem to mind, because I think he know if he exerted himself, he could succeed. However, when my report cards arrived, my parents would always congratulate me and try to make me feel good because I was more often than not in tears. I would be devastated if I didn't have all of the highest marks for my courses. Although my parents never showed us each other's report cards, somehow we always knew. In retrospect, I think they pushed David because it seemed so effortless for him, and they made sure not to push me because I was already pushing myself so hard.

*   *   *

(Christine)

Catherine was her own worst critic. She was very hard on herself if she did not reach the impossibly high academic goals she set for herself. Richard and I felt that all we could ever ask for from our children was that they put their best efforts forward. I knew that Catherine was always working to her maximum potential. Because Catherine was already working so hard, we were careful not to push her any more. I never once had to tell Catherine, or her siblings, to do their homework. The only time we were ever critical of our children's efforts was when we thought David might be goofing off.

*   *   *

(Catherine)

I really appreciated the fact that I was never in direct competition with my siblings. We were never on the same sports teams or in the same after school classes. We all seemed to radiate towards different activities. David was an avid reader, sports fan, writer and artist. I liked playing sports and making crafts. When she was younger, Sarah played the violin and was in a number of plays. In high school, my brother and I did have a few overlapping interests. Most notably, we both loved photography. But because our work was so different, mine ordered and precise versus his more organic and experimental, it did not feel as though we were truly competing.

*   *   *

(Sarah)

Because I was four years younger than Catherine, I had no idea that there was any discussion of learning disabilities until she was in college and I was in high school. I remember her weekly appointments on Friday afternoons when I was young, and I remember thinking that this was to treat her speech impediment, practice so that she would call me Sarah instead of 'Thawa' and that made sense since I knew a few friends who went to tutors or took language lessons outside of school.

My sister loved to play school. To occupy ourselves on the weekend we invented the 'Basement Schoolhouse' where she was the teacher and I, inevitably, was the student. This was my favorite game for a while because I liked having my sister's attention, but also because it fed my already over-inflated childhood ego. None of my friends played school on the weekends, and certainly none of them had been taught long division before the first grade. What I learned from Catherine gained me praise from our parents and allowed me to feel superior to my classmates. Catherine took pride in my bravado as I demonstrated for family friends how I could take square roots or calculate tax percentages as a seven year old. This kind of knowledge and confidence earned me resentment from my classmates and fed a belief that I possessed some kind of genius.

Once I had grown into my hammy dramatic personality around ten, the games we played in the basement changed. I was less interested in doing homework for Catherine, and more interested in creating slapstick scatological skits to entertain the rest of the family. When we were creating a play together, Catherine would often be in charge of the operations and administrative aspects of our performances. She would set up the admissions and ticketing booth, charging a dime or a quarter. She would organize when the curtain would open and close. But when it came to performance, I never questioned that I was in charge. She played the talk-show guest, the back-up singer, and the straight man.

By the time Catherine began applying to colleges, she had created an impermeable world in her bedroom. Piles of papers were carefully placed all over her room. Her desk drawers were immaculately organized, and I had no doubt that she was completely on top of the application process. Around this time, Catherine started being more unpredictable in her moods. She would arrive home after sports practice and close herself in her room for the rest of the night. I painted a large flat rock that I had found for her with white on one side and black on the other, indicating whether or not one should bother knocking on her door. The only way I could ever gain access was if I needed her help. She was always happy to quiz me in my French vocabulary lists or to talk about how to study for a test.

I don't remember hearing the word 'dyslexia' in connection to Catherine until she was in college. I knew that it meant flipping letters when you're reading, but I didn't think that there was any appreciable problem with Catherine since she had already accomplished so much. In fact, I always thought of Catherine as a kind of super-student. I always found writing essays for school difficult, so I figured we had a similar response to David's clear talent with words.

*   *   *

(David)

While reading the first draft of this book, it struck me that I had never realized the degree to which Catherine struggled with dyslexia while we were growing up.

Learning (and, in particular, writing) was always something that came easily to me. I read a lot from a very early age, devouring books as quickly as my parents would buy them for me, and rereading them again and again. Writing was something I always enjoyed, and I remember writing stories as early as kindergarten that I would read to my class at school, or pile up in my drawers at home. In 1987, when I was ten years old, I wrote a 70-page semi-fictional account of the Yankees season on my portable typewriter, interspersing box scores with a fanciful story about a kid my age being kidnapped and kept in Yankee Stadium.

But while I may have guessed that learning wasn't so easy for Catherine (or that she didn't enjoy reading the way I did), she seemed to compensate for it with a manic work ethic and meticulous organization in her room and her studies. While I did my homework each night in a couple of hours, Catherine would sit pouring over her flashcards and writing notes for much longer. Because of her attention to detail, I remember thinking that Catherine was actually a better student than I was. We were raised to believe in a sort of meritocratic system— where hard work would result in greater achievement in the end, -- and it was clear to me that Catherine simply worked much harder than I did.

And while Catherine wasn't particularly good at writing essays (I remember sometimes correcting them to her great consternation), she seemed to make up for this by being an incredibly gifted athlete. She always excelled at sports in a way that I wished I could. While I would get cut from the 8th grade baseball team and the Junior Varsity Basketball Team, year after year, Catherine was regularly the captain of her sports teams at school. She also seemed to have endless capacity to take on extra tasks on the side, serving as the head of our synagogue's youth group, and the head of the yearbook committee among other things. In her last couple of years of high school, she developed a passion for photography as well, and it was clear that she got a lot of creative gratification out of an artistic medium that did not require words.

So the truth is that, while she may have been having a difficult time on the inside, she exhibited all of the outward signs of being totally competent at pretty much everything she put her mind to—even more so than I considered myself.

In some sense it has been a strange and miraculous revelation to watch her put that kind of outgoing competence toward this book (and verbal expression, in general) over the past few years. When she first started writing a blog, it was as though Catherine suddenly was able to write fluidly, in a way I'd never seen her do before—the words coming out as though she were talking to you, which is, in may ways, the true test of good writing. To see her doing crossword puzzles and playing Scrabble without the kind of angst that she would have had with them in earlier years is really wonderful, and this book is kind of the culmination of her overcoming her fear and anxiety about writing.

In my family, we have always had tacit labels. I was "the writer" (or, at times "the actor"), while Catherine was "the athlete" or "the archivist," and Sarah was "the funny one." In watching Catherine complete this book, I admit I've felt certain pangs at watching her diligence to the project, thinking that I might have to relinquish my title as her perseverance outdistances my own current literary output. Hopefully this means I can now discover my innate ability to throw curveballs and become "the athlete," as I'd always wanted.

Extracurricular Activities

Although I was concerned that playing a sport five days a week might take too much time away from my studies, being part of a team turned out to be very valuable for my self-esteem. Had I forgone playing on a team so that I could focus on my studies, I would have probably felt even greater academic frustration. Instead, I was able to explore another side of myself.

In eighth grade, I started playing field hockey, and instantly fell in love with the sport. I also loved the team atmosphere and getting to know some of the older girls on the team. I really admired and respected the head-coach, Ms. Quigley. In the winter, I swam and for two spring seasons, I played softball.

I enjoyed success on the field and in the pool. I know that the success I felt being part of those teams boosted my general confidence levels. Playing sports also helped me to budget my time more effectively. I had less time, so I had to carefully plan how I would use it. As my mother says, an assignment can take up as much time as you have. Meaning, if you have five hours to do a half hour's amount of work, it will take five hours to do if you let it.

Another large part of my life outside of school was being a part of my synagogue's youth group. The Youth Group provided a spiritual outlet as well as a place to socialize away from school. I loved the feeling of connecting to something greater than my little world. Being a part of my synagogue's community reminded me to think of others, to look at life's blessings and to seek balance in my life. And most importantly, to recognize that grades were not all there was to life.

Chapter 5

Study Skills

(Catherine)

Over the years, with the help of my mother, I developed study habits that have helped me earn good grades in most of my high school, college and then graduate school classes. The best word to describe my study method is plodding. Studying for me takes a lot of time and involves continued exposure to the material. I take very detailed and organized notes in class, although sometimes it is hard to hear, process and record everything that is being said as it is said. I love that most of my Business School classes are recorded so I can go back and watch them again if I miss a concept. Over the years I have worked on creating abbreviations for common words, but I have found that this is sometimes even more confusing if I have to figure out what the shorthand means when I am studying later or if I try to reread my notes during class. In the end, I have found that I can reliably abbreviate certain words such as "with," but know that I need to write out the rest. When I review for tests, I begin by re-writing my class notes. Next, I re-read any course readings that might be covered on the test. I take notes while I am reading and then review them when I finish reading the text. After that, I merge my notes from class and the readings. If I feel confident enough that I know something, I leave it off the new study sheet. As I study and learn the material, my study sheets get shorter and more compact. To my chagrin, I go through a lot of paper writing, re-writing and re-writing my notes again. Even if I write really small on old paper and recycle the paper when I am finished, I still hate using so much paper. But I also know that I needed to physically write out the information as many times as necessary in order to really grasp it (re-typing doesn't seem to work for me). On and off I have experimented with just re-reading my notes as a way to study and use less paper, but reading is not as effective as repeatedly reading and then writing the concepts down. Because reviewing is such a long process, I have to start a few days before a test to make sure I get it all in. Cramming, or studying late into the night before a test, has never worked for me. I think it is probably a combination of not having enough time to effectively work-through the information, as well as the anxiety that the last minute studying produces that makes cramming so unhelpful.

I also used and continue to use many flashcards. I keep a list by my bedside where I jot down unfamiliar words I come across in books and magazines. Every so often, I look up these words in a dictionary and make flashcards. Then, to make sure I really understand the word, I make up a sentence with the word in it. I keep the flashcards on my desk in a pretty box so that I remember to look over the cards and learn the words. These vocabulary flashcards serve two purposes: they increase my base vocabulary and they help me to visually recognize the word so when I see it next, I immediately know it. Once I feel confident that I know the word, I put the card in another box and I only check it occasionally.

Writing papers was always much more difficult for me than studying for a test. Looking back, my writing was generally chaotic. I would have plenty of ideas about the topic, having read the book or background material that was required, but no idea how to translate those thoughts onto the paper. Most often, the paragraphs would be filled with arguments that did not relate to each other, pieced together in a haphazard fashion.

I have diligently practiced my writing over the years, and I now know how to make an outline, evaluate it to make sure that the paragraphs logically progress and then how to translate the outline into full sentences that make sense. I often read my finished pieces aloud to make sure it sounds correct, because when I reread it silently, I do not catch nearly as many mistakes. I also know that when I am writing, I need enough time to outline, write the paper and then set it aside for a few days. When I reread a piece, after I have not seen it for a few days, I am a much more critical reader and have a sharper eye for the flow and tone of the paper.

My college roommate, Esther, helped me a number of times in our senior year when I was really stuck writing an essay. She had me talk aloud about the topic while she jotted down what I said. After I had finished speaking, we would look over the notes and she'd help me organize the ideas. I wish I had employed this method much earlier. I had ideas that I could articulate, but somehow they became jumbled between my brain and the paper. With her notes, I could at least start the paper.

I finally got the hang of writing essays in graduate school. I clearly remember something clicking in a history of education course. I was able to not only get out my ideas, but I was also able to think of the essay conceptually and structurally. I could step back and evaluate my work critically without being bogged down by the details. I wish more than anything that I had come to this understanding many years earlier, but the process of learning to write effectively has taught me things I might not have otherwise known or understood. I continue to work on my writing every day in my journal and on my blog. I try to dissect the process and logically set a game plan for myself. I write purposefully and challenge myself to make sure I am being clear at all times.

For this book, I have written many outlines and drafts. To help myself organize the information, I always kept my work in chronological order. I did not necessarily write everything in order, but once I wrote a piece I wanted to include, I would put it in order in my binder so that I could see the progression more clearly and where I needed to add thoughts.

I have always needed absolute quiet to study. Some people study with music playing in the background, but I can't possibly imagine doing that. Luckily, I had my own room until college. When it was time to get to work, I would close the door and turn off the phone. Of course, I needed many breaks, but I chose when to take them instead of being disturbed in the midst of a thought.

(Christine)

I learned early on that I could not just hear something and know it; I have to be actively involved with the learning process to really retain the knowledge. I have to see it, write it out, and get it from multiple sources to be able to cement it in. To this day, when I am at a lecture, I always write down points, even if they are very small, so that I can look back at them. I do not trust myself to just hear the lecture and retain everything.

I have always been very organized: everything has a place so I know where to find it. Chaos does not work for me. I have to have files, folders, post-its and orderly systems for everything. It drives me crazy when people move things on my desk.

In college, I dreaded exams with long two-page written articles that you had to be read and then discussed in an essay. Those kinds of tests would put me over the edge. By the time I had finished reading the prompt, I would have forgotten what I had read about in the beginning.

I gravitated towards medical school because it was not literary and I "got" science. Law school never even vaguely crossed my mind as a possibility. I knew I needed to be more of an action person rather than a writing person. I knew I was never going to write the great novel. I was not going to be a university professor. I was more comfortable doing "practical" hands-on things.

It must have been obvious in some grade ten standardized school test that I had some learning issues because after the test, the teacher came in and said something to the class to the effect of, "all of you in here think that Christine is the smartest person in this grade. But I have news for you, she isn't. She just works really hard." Clearly, a number of my peers had scored higher on this "intelligence test." Her point was that if I could earn 100% on everything, anyone could. At that point, I thought she had blown my cover. I was mortified, but in retrospect, I do not think anyone else noticed or cared as much as I did.

There was one time in eleventh grade when my English teacher turned back a paper and said that it was just unacceptable. He said, "Christine, you have to get your spelling under control." He said I had great ideas, but he simply could not read my paper because of all the errors. I knew at that point that I could not effectively proofread my work because I did not see grammatical and spelling errors. I decided that I was going to have to get the dictionary out for every word that was more than a certain number of letters long. It took me forever to check the spelling in my papers, but I would plod my way through it. In the end, I thanked him for making me do it.

In first year English at University, the same thing happened. I got a D on my first paper. I had never gotten a grade like that, ever. Not even close. I became completely crazed. I wanted to get into medical school and did not want to be retaking this class for the rest of my life. I went to the teacher and said, this is impossible, how could you give me this grade? She said, "Look at the spelling, it is outrageous." I must have slacked on checking each long word in the dictionary. She let me re-write that one paper, but after that, I sweated bullets over every assignment. I remember I wrote very short assignments for the rest of the semester. I vowed that there was going to be no more English ever again. Taking heavy writing courses really exposed my vulnerability.

I am still not sure when a sentence is finished or where to put commas and colons. It is just not obvious to me. It is so interesting to me that my son is a writer and editor because he clearly did not get those skills from me.

Mrs. Putnam

(Catherine)

I credit my eighth and ninth grade English teacher, Mrs. Putnam, with my first writing breakthrough. She never asked me about it, but I think she could tell I had a reading disability by the way I wrote. I will forever be indebted to her for the time she took to help me learn how to write. Before essays were due, I would show her rough drafts and we would discuss how to tighten and organize my ideas. She never wrote any part of the paper for me or told me what to do; she simply coached me along until I realized what needed to be done. It was a slow process, but she stuck with me. She taught me about not repeating words, keeping verbs together and that numerous words could describe the same thing only slightly differently. Mrs. Putnam had spelling and vocabulary lists. Most people hate vocabulary lists, but they were very helpful for me. I avidly memorized the lists with flash cards and by repeatedly rewriting the words with their definitions.

Mrs. Putnam had a list on the chalkboard of words that the class could not misspell in any assignment. The list scared me because I wasn't always sure about spelling, but the fear of misspelling one of them made me work harder to memorize the correct spellings of the words on her list. Many people will see a misspelled word and recognize that it doesn't look right. It might take them a minute to figure out how to fix it, but they know that the original way is incorrect. I rarely recognize misspelled words. Writing it out has never helped me because the word would "look right" no matter how I spelled it. The other strange thing is that once I am aware that I consistently misspell a word, it is even harder to remember the correct spelling because I constantly second guess myself and furthermore, both the correct spelling and the misspelling start to look familiar.

In ninth grade, we were assigned a long research paper about Charles Dickens. Mrs. Putnam systematically laid out how we were to write the paper, what to include, how to list sources and how to start and finish paragraphs. Although I was very nervous about writing the paper, I felt more confident knowing very specifically how to approach it. Throughout the two years I had her as a teacher, Mrs. Putnam allowed me to continue rewriting papers until I had finally written them well. She realized that the best way I was going to learn was by repetition and by dissecting the problems in my work while I corrected them. Instead of assuming that if she pointed out mistakes in one paper, that I wouldn't make the same mistakes next in the next paper, she let me work through the mistakes until they were right. I wish I could have continued to work with her throughout high school and even college.

Around ninth grade, I also realized that I liked to read. As a child, I had never voluntarily picked up a book. I liked being read to, but reading for me had never been pleasurable. In Mrs. Putnam's class, I started to read for fun, not only books I had to read for school.

*   *   *

(Christine)

Around the time that Catherine was in tenth grade, I walked into her room and found her sitting on her bed reading a book for pleasure. I cannot recall what she was reading, but I remember how happy it made me to see her enjoying a book. After that, I noticed books piling up on her bedside table. I was overjoyed that she had finally found pleasure in reading.

Latin

(Catherine)

One of the most frustrating experiences of my life was tenth grade Latin. I had begun learning Latin in seventh grade because it was required at Chapin. My first three years went smoothly. My second and third year, I had a teacher, Mr. Bundy, whom I adored. I looked forward to his class. He was funny, engaging and encouraging. He had been teaching Latin at Chapin for as long as anyone could remember.

In the beginning of the year, Mr. Bundy made up ridiculous nicknames for each student. I was Christine McHair Charts, a combination of some of the letters in my full name, and although my nickname didn't stick, some of his creations live on. I still call my friend Erum, Erumski and Sarah Jane, Junie. He wanted us to feel at ease in his class and enjoy the language.

Mr. Bundy had clear expectations of us. We needed to acquire a certain vocabulary, and how to decline specific verbs. We were also responsible for being able to independently translate any of the passages we had gone over together in class. Before tests and quizzes, he would indicate what to study. Even if he hadn't hinted what to focus on, it was clear to me what I needed to learn. I methodically reviewed and reviewed until I had memorized what we needed to know. The result was consistently good marks. Mr. Bundy averaged my marks at the end of two years: ninety-eight percent. Not too shabby. In order to graduate, each Chapin student had to complete four years of one language (between eight and twelfth grade) or take two years of one language and three of another. I felt that I had a handle on Latin and decided to continue with it instead of starting Spanish. Unfortunately, Mr. Bundy retired to Wyoming after my ninth grade year.

Tenth grade Latin with Mr. Hanson was a completely different story. I started the year expecting a similar rhythm. There were only five of us in the class. I think it might have been Mr. Hanson's first year teaching. During class time, the five of us took turns reading passages and translating them. I enjoyed the literature. It fascinated me that humans struggled hundreds of years ago with the same issues we wrestle with today: love, death and life's purpose.

The first test came and I dutifully prepared, as I had in Mr. Bundy's class, by reviewing, rewriting my notes and reviewing some more. I was ready to go. I walked into class that day and took my seat. Mr. Hanson handed out the test and then sat down at his desk. I perused the test. The panic I experienced as I read through the test is still very real to me. Instead of simply translating sections of the text, as we had done in class, the test had a number of different words in the section underlined. For each underlined word, we had to define the word, say what tense it was in and which person. For a moment, I thought he had given me the wrong test. I had absolutely no idea how to figure out the answers. I had faithfully learned all of the vocabulary and verb tenses the previous years, but somehow it was irrelevant because I did not have a clue about how to apply that knowledge to the current test. My heart began to race and the room got very warm and stuffy. I got up to open the window, and as I returned to my seat, I glanced at my friends. They were busy working on the test. No one appeared panicked or in the least bit sweaty. No one was even looking around the room for clues, although very little was posted on the blackboard or walls. I sat back down and contemplated what to do. I couldn't hand in a blank test. I formed a plan: guess my heart out.

I got most of the test wrong. Even writing about it over ten years later upsets me. I was mortified that I did so poorly. My study method of obsessive reviewing and memorizing in all of my courses had done the trick until now. I was unused to getting bad grades because I always put in a lot of effort. Long ago, I had figured out the equation: lots of studying, rewriting my notes and reviewing them meant I would do well on tests.

A few days after I got the test back and I had composed myself, I spoke to Mr. Hanson. I hadn't been able to speak to him directly for a few days after getting the test back for fear of crying. At our meeting, Mr. Hanson told me to go back and relearn all of the vocabulary and verb tenses from the previous three years. He said if I did that, I would do better next time. I left that first meeting feeling a little better. There was a problem and the proposed solution seemed doable.

Luckily for me, I had saved my old notebooks. I began to review. It was a lot to go over, but each night, I reviewed a few more things. Unfortunately, the next test had the same result. I spoke to Mr. Hanson again who thought I was just not studying enough. This repeated itself a number of times. Nothing is more hurtful than working really hard on something and then being accused of not exerting effort. I asked how I could better prepare for the tests. He said to go over the passages, pick out words and try to decline them. However, the passages were so long and even if I did pick out words, I had no idea if I was right when I declined them. It was especially frustrating that my peers did not seem to experience any of the same tribulations. Granted, I was in a small class with four very bright girls, but I wasn't stupid. I earned good grades in other classes. When I expressed my frustration to them, they suggested studying more. As I have seen time and again, it is extremely difficult for others to empathize when they haven't experience the frustration of not being able to figure something out, when everyone else seems to be able to. Because it came somewhat easily to them after some studying, they were baffled that I encountered so much difficulty. The obvious conclusion was that I just wasn't trying hard enough. Although I was good friends with these girls, I began to secretly despise them a little. I hated the idea that they might think I wasn't as smart as they were or that I didn't try hard enough. After a few attempts to ascertain how they studied so successfully or knew had to figure out the tests, I stopped asking. I did not want them to know how anxious the class made me feel or that I truly could not figure out what exactly we were doing.

At a certain point, after I had tried and tried and continued to fail, I couldn't do it to myself anymore. It is as though my brain automatically tuned out as soon as I walked into that small room and sat in my chair. I never skipped a class, but after a few months of frustration, I was no longer present. I might have been sitting there, but my mind was elsewhere. I even became a little disruptive. I would bring up tangential topics when it was my turn to translate a passage. My favorite not-really-related topic was my brother. I talked about him applying to college, his independent study, and how he too took Latin and was preparing for the Advanced Placement exam in Latin. I got creative in how I changed the subject. I wouldn't just blurt things out like, "My brother is so good at Latin." Rather, I would say, "That reminds me of when my brother was in Nepal last summer…" which would launch me into a monologue about how he hiked and camped and ate yak-butter tea. There was usually a small relevant nugget imbedded in the story that I saved until the last minute. Although I think my classmates enjoyed hearing about my accomplished brother, Mr. Hanson did not appreciate my creative approach to avoiding reading Latin. I was even sent out of the room a few times. I used those opportunities to tour the school, go to the bathroom and catch up on other homework. Being sent out of the room, although slightly embarrassing in front of my peers, was a welcome break. I also knew that it was okay for it to happen a few times, but if it happened too often, Mr. Hanson would tell my advisor and there might be some greater consequence.

Sophomore Slump

Sophomore year did not go well for me. I struggled with the many essays I had to write for English, I disliked my confusing and disorganized Advanced Chemistry teacher and Latin was a constant downer. I experienced my first major depressive episode starting in the winter of my sophomore year, although I did not know what it was at the time. I retreated. I spoke less to my peers and returned home each day as soon as school let out. At home, I was so exhausted that I spent most of my time sleeping. I only got out of bed when it was time for dinner. A few friends said something to me about my reclusiveness, but I brushed them off then avoided them. My parents thought I was moody and were visibly irritated by my behavior. I felt as if a gray cloud were hanging over my head. Nothing I did made me feel better. I no longer wanted to do things I had loved, like swimming and taking pictures. That spring I even decided to quit the varsity softball team, something unthinkable the year before. The only thing I wanted to do was get into my cozy bed and sleep. During school hours, I constantly daydreamed about being wrapped in my warm and fluffy comforter.

Towards the end of the year, I voiced my academic frustrations, particularly concerning Latin to my mother. I am not a big complainer, especially about things that just have to be done, but I flat-out felt that I could not continue this way in Latin. I was constantly confused and my tried-and-true study methods had proved useless. My mother decided to take action. My parents are very loving and supportive. When I was growing up, and even now, they were always available to my bother, sister and me. Unlike other parents of students in my grade, my parents rarely communicated with the school and never lodged complaints, except for the incident in second grade. I do not think they had reason to become involved, because my siblings and I achieved good grades and rarely got into real trouble. When my mother decided to complain about my experience in Latin, I knew it was a big deal. It was also a relief because it indicated that she did not think it was all my fault.

My mother arranged for us to meet with my homeroom teacher, Mr. O'Connor as the end of the spring semester was nearing. We met in a quiet classroom. She spoke about my frustrations with Latin and to my surprise revealed my dyslexia diagnosis. It had not occurred to me that my past reading difficulties had anything to do with my performance in Latin. As was mentioned earlier, when I switched schools, my parents had decided to not tell Chapin about my dyslexia. Why would they, seeing as it had been "fixed." My mother patiently explained to Mr. O'Connor that my specific reading problem was in decoding words and that is what we were doing in Latin class, taking apart words and figuring out all the different parts of them. Mr. O'Connor appeared to listen intently, but when my mother was finished, he simply reiterated that I needed to complete another year of Latin as part of my graduation requirements. I was so thankful to have my mother there with me because she replied in a firm tone that we needed to find another solution. She told him she was not going to let me take Latin for another torturous year. Mr. O'Connor had no suggestions except that I needed to take another year of Latin. Finally, after more back and forth about the graduation language requirement, it surfaced that the one other thing I could do was take a different language for two years. Because of scheduling difficulties, I would have to start Spanish at level 2. Not ideal, but it was better than another wasted year banging my head against the wall.

In retrospect, my difficulty decoding Latin words was a repeat of my difficulty decoding English. When I learned English, I had to memorize the word as a whole. Sounding out a word was useless. Either I knew it or I did not. What Mr. Hanson asked us to do was look at a word and then take it apart to decipher all its components. Unless I had memorized that exact word in that tense, I had no idea how to figure out what the word meant or what tense it was in. The imbedded clues were lost on me.

*   *   *

(Christine)

Up until the middle of tenth grade, Catherine had been progressing well in her studies. She earned high marks and praise from her teachers. By the middle of her sophomore year, however, it seemed that Catherine had hit a wall. She seemed downtrodden in a way that I had not seen before. She was very stressed and a sense of impending doom hung over her, which I interpreted as her acknowledgement that academically she had maxed out her capabilities. When I asked her about it, she mentioned difficulties in a number of her subjects, particularly Latin. I decided that although I rarely got involved in school, that I needed to intervene.

I called a meeting with Mr. O'Connor, Catherine's homeroom teacher, for a few reasons. One of my goals for the meeting was to "out her." Meaning I felt that she had exerted a huge effort across the board and was working to her maximum, and that she should be given credit, especially since she was also working with dyslexia. I really had the sense that her specific academic problems were directly related to her dyslexia. Another thing I wanted to get across in the meeting was that I thought her Latin teacher was inexperienced and unnecessarily hard on her. I felt that instead of guiding her toward figuring out ways to grasp the material, he just told her to study harder, which clearly was not helping. Most importantly, I wanted a plan for next year. School was almost out for the year and I did not want Catherine to have to take Latin again next year.

After we exchanged pleasantries, I explained my reasons for calling the meeting and told Mr. O'Connor about Catherine's dyslexia. Mr. O'Connor paused after I spoke and then said, "That may be all well and good, but there are certain courses she needs to take in order to graduate." This was certainly not the response I had anticipated. I think he thought we were using Catherine's supposed dyslexia as an excuse for a difficult year. It is true that Chapin had no documentation of Catherine's diagnosis, so in retrospect I do not blame his reaction, but it was still surprising that the news of her learning disability did not seem to make him even the slightest bit more understanding or curious. He did not ask me to elaborate or explain her specific diagnosis. I had figured he would say something along the lines of, "Now I see why Catherine might be having some difficulties."

After the meeting, I was not sure that I had made any headway. The best we were going to be able to do was have Catherine switched to take Spanish next year after studying level one Spanish over the summer. I decided that I too wanted to learn Spanish because I had so many Spanish-speaking patients. However, after Catherine and I took a few private lessons, I dropped out.

Chapter 6

Deer Hill

(Catherine)

The academic year had finally ended and I was incredibly relieved to be through with Latin, English and Chemistry, but I was also upset about my grades. Across the board, excluding an A in Photography and Physical Education, I had not done well. My final grade in Latin was the lowest grade I had gotten in my entire academic career. Moreover, I think Mr. Hanson was being nice.

I was incredibly disappointed with myself. I was sure I could have tried harder or done extra credit or *something*. I tortured myself thinking of all the things I could have done better. However, towards the end of grade ten, I had turned off because I could no longer try so hard and continue to fail. Somehow, it was slightly comforting to know that I had gotten bad grades because I had not put in enough effort. It was much easier than realizing that no matter how hard I tried, I was just not going to be able to get the grades I wanted. In a way, it saved my ego a bit to believe that it had been my choice. I had chosen to not work hard enough and the consequence was bad grades. I was mad at myself, but the bad grades did not mean I was stupid. I thought to myself, who needs Latin anyway?

The summer following that dismal year turned things around. I was extremely lucky to have the opportunity to go on a hiking, rafting, community service and camping trip in the

Southwest with a group called Deer Hill. I had always yearned to spend more time in the "wilderness." Aside from a five-day canoe trip the summer before, I had never camped, hiked or whitewater rafted before. Now I was off on a six-week adventure doing all that and more. I believe that is called a baptism by fire.

On the plane ride to Mancos, Colorado, I met, Lizzy, also on her way to joining the Deer Hill group. We chatted, but I was so anxious, that I spent most of the ride pretending to sleep. I did not know then that Lizzy would become one of my dearest and most trusted friends. That summer and countless times afterwards, Lizzy reminded me about being true to myself and enjoying all the wonderful things I could do instead of focusing on what was hard for me. Maybe it is my personality, but I have a tendency to discount my strengths and obsess about my weaknesses. Instead of being pleased with the athletic awards I had won, all I noticed were the less-than-perfect grades.

Our trip had four phases: hiking down into canyons, whitewater rafting, building a dam on a Native American reservation, and hiking in the mountains. It seems so clichéd: a privileged kid from the city goes on a summer wilderness expedition that changes her life forever. Well, it did. I learned on that trip that I had many valuable skills and was an important member of the group. I could not only hike for hours a day through varied terrain with everything I needed on my back, but I could read topographical maps with ease. I found I was a good listener and was adept at quickly setting up camp each evening. I was a team player. They could depend on me and I could on them. Our lives were focused on the present: which turn to take on the trail, where to camp and what to eat. Translating an obscure ancient text never came up. It was just not relevant.

The other kids on my trip came from all over the country and from varied backgrounds. As the trip progressed, we shared more of ourselves. No one had to know that I had bombed that year at school, but I opened up and told some of my friends anyway. I also revealed my depression and feelings of incompetence. I was deeply shamed, but felt relieved once I admitted it. It did not seem to change what they thought of me. My friends listened, shared things about themselves, and validated that of course it was hard to struggle and not succeed. Some of the others even opened up about similar difficulties and expressed how much they appreciated my sharing my own experiences. It was then that I realized that sharing things about my inadequacies might help another person feel better about herself/himself. I liked turning it around. I was helping my friends by opening up.

The thought of our group splitting up and going back to our disconnected lives at the end of the six weeks was very upsetting. Our trip was a finite experience and it was over. I was very reluctant to return home. I even thought that I might prolong the experience just a little bit longer if I was the last person off the flight home. My newly found confidence, and deeper love for the wilderness were strong and I did not want to go back to where I had been before the trip.

When I returned home, I started Spanish lessons at the Institute of Spain. Although there were countless other places I would have rather been that August, I constantly repeated the inner mantra, "This is much better than Latin." I would say it over and over again in my head as I walked through the hot, smelly streets to class. I knew that taking Spanish was the best means to an end that my mother and I had been able to devise.

I started the school year with renewed spirit. Field hockey preseason started two weeks before the school year and I was happy to be with my friends on the field. It was also a huge boost when my team voted me a co-captain. As for academics, I made the decision that I could do well if I set my mind to it. I was signed-up for the most rigorous classes and really lucked out with teachers that year. I was determined to make it a good year.

*   *   *

(Christine)

Catherine clearly did not want to be back in New York City after her summer away with Deer Hill. Sarah and I went to the airport to meet her. Catherine and her friend Kevin were the last ones off the plane, although I knew she had been seated in the middle of the plane. She did not talk much on the car ride to Long Island where we were going to spend a week together as a family. When we got there, Catherine insisted on sleeping outside, but I refused to let her. She also got extremely upset when we washed her clothes from the trip and was nearly hysterical when Marina accidentally bleached the sun hat she had worn on the trip.

I do not think I understood until recently what an important experience that summer away had been for her. Nor did I realize how difficult it was for her to re-enter her old life. I thought she just wanted to sleep outside because she liked the outdoors and I didn't let her because I thought it was unnecessary and unsafe. I also did not grasp the degree of trepidation she had about starting another school year.

My advice to other parents would be: create as many winning scenarios as possible for your children. On her Deer Hill program, Catherine was away from her regular environment and got to challenge herself in new ways. She found real success in a realm other than academics. I know she still cherishes that summer.

Composition

(Catherine)

Although I returned to New York ready and willing to give it my best shot junior year, I still encountered problems with my writing compositions. Here are a few comments that my eleventh grade English teacher, Mr. O'Connor, wrote on various writing assignments: "Catherine—You have a number of mechanical errors that need to be addressed. Of particular concern are the number of fragments, which make their way into your otherwise excellent writing. Be careful." (B+) And another: "Catherine—It is clear you spent a lot of time reworking this essay, and you have improved significantly the integration of quotations and the fluid presentation of your ideas. Your organization still needs work, however, and you need to be sure that your focus remains squarely on your thesis. Nevertheless, a solid effort!" (B+)

SATs

In eleventh grade, my school gave the PSATs so we could practice taking the SAT, a standardized test some colleges required for admission. I looked over and tried some old tests in a big study guide before the PSATs. I did okay on the practice SAT, but my language score was noticeably lower than my score in math.

My parents agreed to get me a tutor to help study for the real SAT. I didn't need help in math, but I really needed some assistance with the reading comprehension section. I think I had six sessions one on one with the tutor. In the sessions, she went over what types of questions would be on the test and strategies for answering the questions. She showed me how to dissect the language of the question to get clues. She also showed me how to eliminate some choices and how to make sure I was picking the best answer. She helped me read, understand and take notes on the long passages. She taught me how to underline phrases and how to go back and reread sections before answering the question. Armed with the tools she taught me, I did well on the language section when I took the real SAT.

I have very little faith in the predictive nature of standardized tests. The SATs are supposed to correlate with academic achievement in college, but how can that be when specifically studying for the test produces higher scores? Once I understood what types of questions would be on the test and how to approach them, I was so much more comfortable and relaxed taking the test.

On the old SAT, there were no short-answer or essay questions. However, colleges required taking at least three specialized tests, called SAT II's, to show competence in different academic areas. One of the SAT II's they wanted was a writing competency test. I sweated bullets over that one. The writing test was an hour-long and consisted of some questions about grammar and three short essays. My SAT tutor came back to help me prepare for that test. Although I had been writing papers for years, grammar was still very challenging for me. I was beginning to use it correctly in my work, but it was way too much to ask me to look at passages and identify grammatical mistakes or give the correct part of speech. Even with the tutoring, I was still very fuzzy on the grammar. On and off since seventh grade, I had been attempting to learn the rules of grammar, but it never seemed to stick. The only way I learned grammar was by practicing it in my writing. I got a 680 out of a possible 800 on the writing test. My SAT subsections and other

SAT II's had all been higher. I debated taking the test over, but was hugely relieved when my mother told me not to. She said the score was good and I had too many other things to do to waste my time focusing on grammar and studying for the test. I was incredibly relieved that she made the decision for me. It was very kind of her. I probably would have spent many hours studying, retaken the test, and not have done much better.

The College Essay

I started working on my college essays in eleventh grade. I figured if I had enough time, I might be able to write something really stellar. Our school's guidance counselor had scared the bejesus out of me by mentioning that the essay was one of the most important pieces of the application. The personal essay was our chance to "sparkle" and show the admissions officers who we really were. This proposed essay would somehow let them know that I was a serious student who knew how to write really well and had had many meaningful experiences I could bring to their school. This essay would communicate that although I worked hard at school, I was also a good person who was committed to helping other people. In my mind, the essay would definitely not indicate my struggle with dyslexia; although that was probably the hardest thing I had had to overcome to get to the point of applying to college.

I wasn't sure how to begin. I thought of some of the more significant experiences in my life and jotted down ideas. Our counselor had warned us not to write about the four D's: death, disease, dying, and dogs so I refrained from writing about my fear of dogs, the death of my very special grandmother and my father's fear of dying. Writing about disease hadn't really crossed my mind, except to note how incredible is was that after so many years of subway riding, I had yet to contract a virulent form of some obscure disease. Once those topics were off the list, I was at a loss. One essay I wrote was about how I had started a jewelry business when I was eleven. I described how I created the pieces, marketed them at craft fairs, priced the pieces, kept careful logs of all the transactions and then expanded my operations over time. I thought it showed ingenuity and perseverance, my English teacher thought it was a little stale. He wanted me to write about something current. Over the summer, I continued to work on the essays. For one essay, I wrote about my experience as an office slave in an investment-banking firm that summer. Highlights of that job included excessive air-conditioning, a tote bag and a creepy banker asking me on a date. I had also acquired some really superior clock watching abilities that summer. I tried to turn the experience around and focus on my not so vital role in managing client portfolios and doing minor stock research. Writing, then proof reading, that essay bored me to death. Honestly, one of the most meaningful experiences had been the six-week hiking expedition the summer before. The trip had pushed my physical limit, expanded my horizons, renewed my spirit and had given me a huge confidence boost. I worried that it was cliché that a New York City girl went into "the wilderness" and found herself. I struggled to communicate how that experience had changed me. By this point, it was a month into my senior year and my panic was rising.

Until senior year, my mother had been helping me proofread my essays. Aside from a few teachers, I would not allow anyone else to even glance at the essays. I was extremely embarrassed by my writing. I showed my mother because she was a less critical reader than my father. I knew that editing was important, but before I got to that, I needed to know if the content was good. If I showed Dad my writing, he would immediately point out the misspellings and grammatical mistakes. He once explained, when I asked him to focus on content versus spelling and grammar, that his eye was drawn to mistakes and they distracted him. I often wondered if he actually read and comprehended what I wrote, because when I got back my work from him, it was always covered with corrections. After my mother had read and reread this one essay, I felt confident enough to show my brother. I even thought it was pretty good. David is a naturally gifted writer, so I thought he could help polish my masterpiece.

Just because someone is a good writer, it does not necessarily follow that they are a good editor of another person's work. My brother was young and an excellent writer, but he had not yet learned how to edit another person's work without making it his own.

My college essay was almost unrecognizable when he gave it back to me. He had edited it so much, that it no longer even sounded like me. In essence, he had written a new essay. I was crushed. Had it been that bad that it needed to be completely rewritten? My last shred of confidence in my writing vanished.

Although it was tempting for a brief moment to use the uber-edited version, I knew it was not my voice and it was cheating to use the essay for my applications. Even more than that, I did not want to be admitted to a college that I hadn't earned acceptance to. I adamantly wanted to get in on my own merits so that I would never question whether I had earned my place. It was more important to me to honestly earn a spot at a school then to get into a school on false pretenses. I scrapped that essay and started again. By this point, I was completely hysterical.

I do not remember much about the essays I finally wrote. I must have blanked out the entire experience. The only thing I remember is that for the month of December I exclusively ate Coco Krispies and could not sleep because I was so agitated. There were also nightly tears that would be temporarily relieved with dance parties I held in my room. When I was going to explode, I would put on "Right Back Where We Started From" by Maxine Nightingale loud enough for my parents and sister to hear which would signal them to come in and dance.

The parents of some of my friends helped them to fill out their college applications, but I wanted to do it by myself. I wanted the applications to look just right and I worried that if I delegated any of the responsibilities that something might go wrong. I applied to fourteen schools. I had not set out to apply to that many, but my guidance counselor said I needed more safety schools, because I was not going to get into the "top-tier" schools I was looking at. Just filling in all of the blanks on fourteen applications took a long time. The essays took much longer.

*   *   *

(Christine)

When it came time for Catherine to start the process of applying to college, Richard and I stood back and let Catherine lead the way. She decided the schools she wanted to visit, she planned the tours, and did the applications herself. She also decided that she only wanted one parent to accompany her on the campus visits because she felt it was too overwhelming to have both of us there giving our opinions. Richard visited most of the schools with Catherine. I was confident that Catherine would approach to process of applying to college the same way that she approached everything else she did: in an organized and timely manner. Richard and I tried our best to not express any opinions about the schools she had chosen to apply to, instead taking on the role of being supportive in whatever capacity she wanted.

Senior Year

(Catherine)

Aside from the heinous process of applying to college, I enjoyed my busy senior year of high school. My small school had allowed me to flourish in many areas. In addition to my Advanced Placement classes, I was editor-in-chief of the yearbook, president of my Synagogue's youth group, and co-captain of both the field hockey and swim teams. I felt as though I had gained respect for being honest, hardworking and a team player.

April rolled around and college acceptances started coming in. I had gotten into eleven schools and was wait listed at two of the fourteen schools I had applied to. I figured that they must not have weighed the essays as heavily as my guidance counselor had said they would. Two schools even offered me academic scholarships. All that hard work, each and every night for so many years, had been worth it because now I could choose where to spend the next four years. After receiving all of the acceptances, I promptly destroyed all evidence of the essays. There was no need to ever revisit them.

After much thought and weighing of my options, I thought I was going to attend Duke University. Before sending in the check, my parents wanted me to go re-look at some of the other schools. Secretly, I think they thought the campus was a little too far from home. I took a day off from school and my mother, father and I drove up to Amherst, Massachusetts. My mother had never seen the campus because my father and I had done most of the college tours together. On the tour, the guide explained Amherst's open curriculum. Aside from taking a required freshman seminar, there were no core curriculum requirements. When we heard that, my mother and I turned to each other and mouthed: no language requirement. How incredible! I can understand the argument that having core requirements forces students to explore various disciplines that they might not otherwise pursue, but I didn't want to waste my time crying through another language. I definitely wanted to take a broad range of classes, and I did, but I was relieved that I wouldn't be forced to take a language. Then and there, I knew that Amherst was the school for me.

College Acceptance

(Richard)

The college admissions process must be agony for everyone, parents and students alike, but thankfully it was made easier by Catherine's super organized approach: she had files with labels and checklists for everything. Catherine and I visited several colleges together before her senior year. She and I went without Christine and it was a wonderful opportunity to bond in a way that we had never had before. It was also obviously less stressful for Catherine to not have both parents with her. She kept very detailed records of her impressions of the schools we visited.

When her acceptance letters came, I was particularly thrilled by her acceptance to Duke University, which I thought of as a large, diverse, social and athletic campus. I thought her multiple talents would find a place there. Instead, at the last minute, after another visit, she chose Amherst with its super academic and intellectual focus, which to me seemed a little scary, especially with her difficulty writing. But it was her choice and I supported her decision, even if I had my reservations.

Chapter 7

Freshman Year

Going off to college was a time of extreme anxiety for me. I recognize that most students going off to college are apprehensive about the transition. They worry about making new friends and leaving good friends behind. I worried about that too, but I was much more concerned about the new academic expectations. Carroll and Iles (2006) found that dyslexic students in higher education show anxiety levels that are much higher than their non-dyslexic peers. They recommend that the emotional well being of learning disabled students be a part of the assessment of needs for the student entering college and receiving support services instead of simply addressing the academic needs. In contrast to the frequent assignments I had in high school, many of my new courses gave final grades based on a few long essays or written examinations. My anxiety surrounding writing had not vanished when I was accepted into college. In fact, it intensified. I could no longer rely on rewriting or getting points for class participation. It was an all or nothing deal and it scared me to death.

When I got to Amherst and everyone was so smart, confident and accomplished, I wanted to turn right around and go home. How was I going to make it? I had given it everything I had to get through high school. I did not see how I could work any harder. In retrospect, a year off might have been a good idea, so I could have enjoyed what I had accomplished before jumping right into the next endeavor.

A big part of my difficult transition to college was feeling incompetent and just not smart enough. I feared that they had mistakenly admitted me. Maybe they meant to accept another Catherine, had sent the acceptance letter unintentionally to me, then realizing their mistake decided they could not un-admit me. My first semester, I read an article in one of the college's magazines about the admissions process. In the article, one of the Deans of Admissions said something to the effect of, "We don't admit anyone who should not be here." I cut out the quotation and taped it to the bottom of my desk drawer. Reading that quote always made me feel just a little bit better on those tough days when everything felt impossible.

Midway through my first semester, I went to meet with my advisor, Professor Rose Olver. We spoke about my course selections for the next semester. I voiced my fear that Amherst had mistakenly accepted me. She took out my file, looked it over carefully then looked me straight in the eyes and said in a firm tone: "You got in with flying colors. There was no mistake." I will never forget that moment. Although I did not fully believe her, it was incredibly comforting to hear that I was meant to be at Amherst.

It is painful looking back at my journal from my first semester. My journal had many entries about how panicked I was about some assignment. Many times, I got myself so worked up about an essay that I was unable to work on the paper at all. I would have to take a break, go for a walk, take a shower, or write in my journal until I had calmed down enough to try again.

Although Amherst did not have any core course requirements when I attended, they did require that each freshman sign up for a freshman seminar. The seminar was only for first semester freshmen. The college wanted all freshmen to have some guided writing course at the beginning of their tenure. I am not sure how I was placed into mine, because I am sure it was neither my first, second, third, fourth or fifth choice. My seminar focused on identity through weekly writing assignments. I slaved over these autobiographical pieces. I wrote truthfully and from my heart about my family, my friends and my deepest desire to make a positive impact on the world. I also wrote poems about love and heartache.

Getting the assignments back was devastating. They were mercilessly marked all over the place with his hateful red marker. I went to the professor to ask how I could do better. He said my organization was off and my stories did not flow. Okay, great, I thought, just tell me what to do! He would not let me try to re-write them, he just wanted me to apply these new insights to my next assignments. I was crushed. I had counted on re-writing papers all through high school. If I did not get it right the first time, I just kept trying and trying until it was right (or at least acceptable). It was much harder for me to take the comments from one assignment and apply them to the next because each paper I wrote I felt as though I were beginning from scratch. He said I needed better organization of my thoughts, but I was not sure how to do that. I started going to the writing center with all of my work. It helped and I credit the writing center with saving some of my dignity. Nevertheless, as much as they assisted me, they could not write the papers for me. Sometimes I felt as though I was banging my head against a wall, repeatedly. As soon as one big paper was finally complete, there was another one to start on. And I started on papers as soon as I could. If I left an assignment for the night before it was due, it was an assured failure. The combination of the general anxiety about writing and the time crunch would upset me so, that I wouldn't be able to think clearly, which was of course evident in the final result. I never once asked for an extension in college. I think it was a matter of mistaken pride.

*   *   *

(Christine)

Catherine had a very difficult time adjusting to college. Her difficulties adjusting seemed more dramatic than other students' reactions to the same situation. Richard went up to visit once on a weeknight to help calm her down and brainstorm on how to make it work. In truth, we were not sure how things were going to go and if Catherine was going to be able to stay at Amherst. She was stressed to the limit. I did not make the connection at the time that a good portion of her stress was related to academic difficulties associated with her dyslexia. We took that first semester day by day, and let Catherine lead the way on whether or not she felt that she could stay at Amherst. I was so glad she had chosen a school close to home so that we could be there in three hours if we needed to be.

*   *   *

(Catherine)

I was not at all surprised when, as I was doing research for this book, I came across the work of J.S. Pickering, who asserts "college is rarely a carefree time for [learning disabled] students. Often they describe these years as highly stressful." [22]

---

[22] J.S. Pickering (2002) Signals of Learning Disabilities at Various Developmental Stages. Montessori LIFE Summer. Pp. 46-48.

Slow and laborious reading and writing in contrast to the ability to comprehend materials at a college level makes getting through course material incredibly challenging. I really enjoyed my courses. I love learning new things and the discussions in class. I have always participated in discussions whether it is offering an idea or challenging someone else's. My biggest problem was getting through the course materials and composing my thoughts onto paper.

General College

College was a mixed time for me. Socially, I had a fantastic time. I made some incredible friends and was exposed to many new ways of thinking. Academically, I was frustrated a lot. I enjoyed my classes and learned a great deal, but when it came to expressing my thoughts in papers, I really struggled.

At home, I had been able to close my door and be frustrated by myself. In college, there were always people around. Even on the lower level of the library, I was bound to bump into someone. It was hard to find a way to release all of my anxiety and frustration.

My parents knew that college was very stressful for me. Whenever my mother would call, which she did every other day (I convinced her that every day was too often), the first thing she would ask was; "What have you done for fun recently?" And she really wanted to know. She wanted to hear that I had taken time to enjoy myself. My mother understood my proclivity for endless studying and instead of asking me about my assignments, she made a point of encouraging me to have more fun. My mother also believed that I had to look at college as though it were a full-time job. She thought I should set boundaries on how much time I could spend studying. Just like a nine-to-five job, after work, I was free to do other things.

Joining the crew team was one of the best choices I made in college. I absolutely loved and looked forward to being on the water six days a week. Even when it was cold and wet, I couldn't wait to get in the boat. Although crew is the quintessential team sport, it is also a solitary sport. Everyone in your boat has to be stroking at the same time for the boat to glide smoothly in the water, but you do not look at your teammates or even talk to them while rowing. Instead, you stare at their backs the whole time. I did not have to pretend to be cheerful or even smile while I was on the water. I just had to pull my weight in time. The rhythmic stroking became a kind of meditation, just as swimming had been for me in high school. I have found very few things in life as satisfying as the sound of eight oars entering the water then stroking in time.

*   *   *

In college, I lived with four talented and sometimes intense girls. I guess I should have predicted that most people at Amherst would be slightly hyperactive over-achievers. I am like a sponge in that I absorb the emotions of the people around me. When someone is upset, I get upset too. It is the same with stress. Not only was I worried about my own work, I also got anxious when my friends were anxious about their work.

One of my roommates was already an accomplished journalist when she started Amherst. She had even had pieces published in USA Today! I was awed, amazed and more than a little intimidated. I couldn't image writing something that would be accepted by a major newspaper. Another roommate also wrote, but she wrote incredible short stories when she was not working on her pre-med classes. My roommate for all four years of college was an amazing tennis player as well as artist and designer (she designed the cover of this book!). In addition, my fourth roommate was an excellent economics and foreign language student. Sometimes I wished I had lived with a few average achievers, so that when I compared myself, I did not feel so inferior.

Ramapo-Anchorage Camp

The summer after sophomore year, I worked at an amazing sleep-away camp for emotionally disturbed youth, which was then called Ramapo-Anchorage, located in Rhinebeck, New York. I was getting more interested in learning disabilities from my psychology courses and thought it would be a good way to make a positive impact on some kids' lives while learning more. I had no idea it would be so hard. In my cabin I had boys who had been abused, one with ADHD and Tourettes, one who was on the autistic spectrum, another who saw little aliens and one who only talked about yo-yo's. Although my boys all had different issues, it was my job to make my bunk into a team. We had cheers and played other bunks in basketball. During our nightly bunk meetings we would talk about the day, give meaningful compliments and brainstorm how things might have gone better. My heart broke over and over again as I watched them struggle to form relationships and cope with the world. I could sense their frustration and it reminded me a little bit of my own frustrations learning how to read. They could sense they were a little different, but did not want to be, but also didn't know how to be any other way. The biggest heartbreak came at the end of each three-week session when I had to let them go. Camp was an oasis for them, a place just for fun. As they boarded the buses to go home, I couldn't help crying knowing that they were going back to some of the same tough situations and that nothing I could do could make it any better after they had gone.

I met one of my closest friends, Lisa, that summer. She was always positive and playful, even after dealing with a tough situation, such as restraining a child. I also realized watching her and how she interacted with her cabin, that she had a very specific gift that I did not possess. She was able to fluidly understand and deal with all of her boys' issues, while not letting them affect her too much. She maintained an amazing perspective throughout the summer. I knew she could tell it was hard for me and let me know in her joking way that she was there for me.

Junior Year

The second semester of my junior year, I planned to spend studying art in Florence. I took introductory Italian first semester at the University of Massachusetts so that I would not be completely lost when I got there. Because it was a large, introductory course, I did fine. Italian is also know as a fairly transparent language, meaning that there are not many exceptions to rules and each phoneme reads the same way each time you see it. Dyslexics appear to have an easier time learning transparent languages.

Before I started my semester abroad, I traveled with my mother and Marina to Southern India to visit one of the eye hospitals my mother works with. It was not my first choice to go to India at this time, but my mother was very excited about the trip. Looking back, I can see clearly that I was depressed. That fall, I had started sleeping a lot and had retreated from a number of activities that I enjoyed. Working at camp had been such an intense experience and I'd barely had time between the end of camp and school starting to really decompress. And although I really loved my roommates, I was feeling claustrophobic and tried to avoid their wanting to eat every meal together or go to the gym at the same time. I desperately wanted time alone.

*   *   *

(Christine)

I was worried about Catherine. After her first semester of junior year, it seemed that she had been neglecting herself and she seemed angry. I thought this trip to India would be a good break for her and a chance for her to get a hold of herself before starting her semester in Florence.

Richard met Catherine and me in Florence a few days before her program was to begin. One evening, before meeting a friend, the only person we knew in Florence, for dinner, we sat Catherine down. We told her that we were concerned. We mentioned her bad skin (and that she didn't even try to cover it up with make-up), that she had put on weight, wasn't smiling much and that she looked unattractive with her shorter haircut. We told her that this semester away was going to be a time for her to reinvent herself and start fresh. In truth, we were very worried about leaving her in this state so far away from home and with no back up except a not-so-close family friend who lived in the city. We felt that maybe if we gave her this major disapproval that it would help Catherine muster up the strength to get through this semester. Richard and I had also worried that we had done Catherine and her siblings a disservice by not being more critical when they were younger. As opposed to my upbringing, where I was constantly criticized for small and irrelevant things, Richard and I feared that we had not been critical enough. This "talking to" was our attempt at tough love.

*   *   *

(Catherine)

The last straw was when my parents sat me down and told me I needed to be someone else, or at least pretend to be. They pointed out all my physical flaws and then expected me to magically feel better and take life by the horns. It took a huge amount of effort to just get dressed in the morning. There was no way I was up for reinventing myself.

Two days into the program and without telling anyone, I packed my bags and headed for the airport. I switched my flights and got myself home within two days. I must have looked upset because nice looking people kept stopping to ask me if I needed help or if I was okay. Coming home at this time in my life was one of the best decisions I ever made. Although I was deeply depressed, I also felt empowered that I could change things if they were not right. Instead of sticking it out in Florence for the semester like I was supposed to, I made the choice to take the time off and work on me. It wasn't quitting so much as recognizing what I needed to do for myself. I also knew that it would mean I would have to do an extra semester after most of my friends had graduated.

In college when you live so closely with your peers and have almost everything provided for you, it is easy to lose perspective. Your job while in college is to learn and complete assignments. Although I had always had a student job while at Amherst, I had lost perspective. I was measuring myself against my peers and feeling as though I fell short. What I knew but did not know was that I was part of a select group that had gotten to go to college at all and that some of the "stress" was simply a by-product of being in such close quarters.

I started therapy the week I got back. Instead of pretending that leaving had solved the problem, when the study abroad program wasn't the problem at all, I knew that there were deeper issues bothering me and that I needed to take the time to analyze them before I could move on. I got a job working in the Photo Department of the Associated Press. No, I was not the one taking the pictures. Instead, I was making sure that all of the subscribers got the pictures that the contracted photographers had taken. It wasn't a glamorous or overly exciting job, but I liked it and I made money. Working full-time also reminded me that I was capable. I could do this full-time job well and support myself.

When I returned to college the next fall, I was refreshed and excited to be there. I couldn't wait to start my courses. Overall, I was calmer and more grounded. I also did much better in my courses and felt more able to take on challenges.

*   *   *

(Christine)

Richard and I were very surprised when Catherine just showed up one afternoon in New York when she was supposed to be off studying in Florence. We had been nervous when we were not able to reach her, but assumed she was busy with her new courses. We had no idea that she had packed up her things and decided to fly home. In retrospect, I am proud and pleased by Catherine's response to the situation. She recognized that it was not going to work for her and she made a change on her own. Although she was in distress, she figured everything out herself.

Career Choices

(Christine)

Catherine recently asked me if my trouble with dyslexia had influenced my career path. Although I did not know I was dyslexic, I had a good understanding of my strengths and weaknesses as a student. By the end of high school, I knew that although I was getting the hang of writing, it did not come naturally and that I would not do well in a field where I needed to write a lot. I think I fell into medicine by process of elimination. Once I eliminated all fields, such as being a professor, that required a lot of writing and/or that I was not interested in, I was down to science. I liked science, it made sense to me and (unless I became a researcher) as a doctor I would be working with patients instead of writing. Luckily, I have really enjoyed my career as an ophthalmologist.

*   *   *

(Catherine)

By the end of college, I knew I did not want to pursue a career in a writing-intensive field. I also knew that I did not want to be stuck behind a computer eight hours a day for the rest of my life. During college I had worked as a photographer for the regional newspaper. While I loved photography and one of my majors was in Fine Arts, I wasn't sure if I was good enough to make it a career. It was also important to me that I work at a job where I felt I was contributing to society's greater good and where I was directly affecting peoples' lives. Teaching (and possibly school administration one day) seemed like a good choice. I love working with children and knew I could be creative while supporting myself. From my summer experiences working with children, I also knew that every day would be different.

Learning About Dyslexia

In my freshman year, I took Developmental Psychology with Professor Rose Olver, who was also my academic advisor. In the course, we briefly discussed different learning difficulties in relation to the "normal" trajectory of human growth. One of the topics covered was dyslexia. I honestly had not thought much about my dyslexia for a long time, nor could I remember when I first heard the term used in association with my own problems. I had thought about my difficulties writing and wishing I could construct a well-written essay, but somehow it was not linked in my mind to the dyslexia diagnosis. I remembered the tutoring, but I guess I thought my difficulties only had to do with reading and that I had been "fixed". Our course textbook described the disorder and made me aware that dyslexia was not just a reading problem, it also affected my ability to spell and write clearly. I was stunned by this new information. As I thought back to high school and before, I realized that I had always had a very hard time with spelling, grammar and organizing my writing. It was as though a light-bulb had gone off and I finally understood that it was all connected to the same glitch in my wiring. I remember calling my mother to tell her what I had learned and reflecting with her how it all made sense and how everything was connected.

As a result of that class, I wanted to know more about dyslexia. I believe my interest was one of the reasons I chose to major in Psychology as well as Fine Arts. Dyslexia was discussed in a few more of my Psychology courses including Assessment and Abnormal Psychology, but it was not until the second semester of my senior year that I had a chance to immerse myself in learning specifically about dyslexia. In the fall of 2001, I applied to volunteer at the Laboratory for the Assessment and Training of Academic Skills (LATAS) at the nearby University of Massachusetts, Amherst campus. The lab, run by Professor Royer, had three main goals: 1) to develop assessment procedures that can be used to identify the nature of learning difficulties experienced by individuals with learning difficulties, 2) to develop educational procedures that will help students improve their academic performance, and 3) to develop a fundamental understanding of the nature of learning difficulties. LATAS had developed a unique computer program, which aimed to assist dyslexic children by training them to correctly identify phonemes. I could not wait to start work. One of the laboratory assistants showed me the lab and I observed him running a session with a child. The child and the lab assistant faced a computer screen. One at a time, nonsense words popped up on the screen. The student would say the nonsense combination as fast as he/she could. The lab assistant had a box. If the student had pronounced the sounds correctly, the assistant would press the green button. If the random combination of letters were mispronounced, the assistant would press the red button. Speed was also important. The faster the child said the nonsense "word", the better score they would achieve. At the end of the session, the computer tabulated how many answers were correct and how long the session took and then compared the numbers to a predetermined norm. These numbers were then plotted on a longitudinal graph. I was a little nervous watching the test because I realized I might have difficulty accurately testing the children, but I figured I would practice and be fine. I was surprised when Dr. Royer asked me to take the test myself so that I could understand what the students were doing. I took the test. Compared to third graders from around the nation, I scored in the 38th percentile for phonemic awareness. It was a long, awkward moment after the score popped up on the screen. To break the uncomfortable silence I blurted out, "I'm dyslexic." He replied, "No kidding."

The test blew my mind. I was a few months shy of graduating from college (one of the top Liberal Arts colleges in the country), and I had scored in the lower half of third graders nation-wide in decoding ability. The test made it even clearer to me that although I had learned effective coping strategies; I was still deficient in phonemic awareness skills. I still had dyslexia. Bruck (1992) tested dyslexics at all ages and found that even in adulthood, dyslexics do not acquire appropriate levels of phoneme awareness. She went on to say that, it is not that dyslexics acquire phoneme awareness at a slower rate than normal readers do; they simply never acquire age-appropriate levels of the skill. Luckily, tasks that require specific phoneme awareness/decoding skills are rare in "the real world."

Dr Royer allowed me to work in his lab, but asked that I memorize the list of nonsense words that the computer generated so that I could accurately score the students. That seemed more than fair. I went over the list with the lab assistant and he helped me figure out the right way to pronounce each "word." I tried to write it out so that when I was reviewing, I would be memorizing the correct pronunciation. I worked in the lab a few hours a week and was able to sit in on the research assistants' weekly meeting. I enjoyed learning more about the disorder and current research, but it was also pretty upsetting for me to see children struggling so much. Many of the children who came into the lab had experienced years of failure and I could tell by their postures that they felt diminished. I tried to be as cheerful, warm and welcoming as possible, without being fake and annoying. A few of the parents seemed to appreciate hearing that I too am dyslexic, and was soon to graduate from college. The road can look bleak to parents with children who have learning disabilities. It is truly frustrating for everyone involved.

I observed that the parents and students really liked to see their accuracy and time scores graphed. Laid-out on a graph, they could see that the child was making progress. I too liked the concrete results. With definable results, we could see we were achieving something and not just working in a void.

During this time, I was deciding what I wanted to do after college. I knew I was interested in dyslexia, I had always gravitated towards helping other people and I loved children. It seemed obvious that I should work with dyslexic children. However, when I thought of my experience in the lab, I wondered if it would be too personal and emotionally exhausting. I thought back to the summer after sophomore year that I spent as a counselor at an overnight camp for emotionally disturbed youth. That experience was draining, and I worried that devoting myself to helping dyslexic children might have the same effect. It also became clear to me that although I had the desire to help other dyslexics, I did not have the capacity to master the mechanics of language and the intricacies of phonemic awareness that is needed for the job.

Following my graduation in December of 2001, a good friend and I moved into a very cute apartment in Northampton, Massachusetts. Everything should have been perfect: I had good friends, I just graduated from college, I had a temporary job and the future was wide open. Instead, I was crippled with self-doubt and panic about the future and about my abilities. I fell into another deep depression. This episode was more intense than the previous ones. I was incapable of functioning. I spent days staring at the ceiling, unable to get myself out of bed. I was exhausted, but wide-awake. I did not feel qualified to do anything and each time I thought about a new endeavor, I became overwhelmed thinking about even beginning it. My parents were worried, so one night my brother and father drove up to bring me home.

By the end of February, I was feeling a little better. I was working with a therapist, the same one who had helped me two years earlier, to regain some perspective. She reminded me of my accomplishments, and how they had seemed so insurmountable in the beginning. She also pointed out that I had gone through this before and that I'd come out of it in time and not to push too hard, instead to be nice to myself and use the time to sort though and figure out what was at the heart of the depression. She also made me think about life in little steps, not giant overwhelming ones.

Although my boyfriend of a few months, Bobak, and I had broken up when I graduated, we were still in touch and he was incredibly supportive of my work to get past this depressive episode. He was spending the semester in Sydney, Australia and suggested I come for a visit when he had a break in March. I thought about it for a few minutes and then decided to take a chance. I had never been to Australia and did not know anyone, aside from my father's friend, who lived there. I was feeling a whole lot better by then and the thought of an adventure really helped lift my spirits even further.

I spent about a third of my time in Australia traveling with Bobak another third traveling with first a friend from high school, Anna, who I randomly ran into in a hostel in Tasmania, and then about a third of the time I was on my own. Like my experience the summer away in high school with Deer Hill, backpacking in Australia was one of the best experiences of my life. I saw a tremendous amount of the country and re-learned many things about myself. The trip reminded me that I was capable of making things happen. I had no itinerary and only thought a day or two in advance, but I could take care of myself. Most importantly, it renewed my spirit and made me feel that I could handle whatever came my way. What was supposed to be three weeks turned into eight and I only came home because my grandmother was flying in from Vancouver to see me walk in Amherst's May graduation. My plane touched down in JFK two days before I received my diploma.

Teaching

When I returned home from Australia, I did not really have an idea what I wanted to do for a job. I moved home and worked at a day camp in June that I had worked at for a number of summers. At the end of the session, I mentioned to the director that I would be interested in teaching if any spots opened up. And I think of it as pure luck that two spots opened up that August and that I got to work at the Episcopal School, a fantastic Manhattan preschool, along with Kate, one of my closest friends from high school.

I was not sure initially how I would like teaching, but as the year progressed I realized that I loved it. I loved watching the wheels turn as students learned. I also really enjoyed the creativity of planning projects that were fun but also helped my students work on their skills. I loved getting to know each child's strengths and areas that needed a little work. I was particularly drawn to students who had trouble with rhyming, difficulty learning the letters of the alphabet, trouble sequencing events and difficulty associating sounds with letters; all things that are signs in preschool that the child might have a language disorder. When I taught older grades, language problems were more pronounced with some students having trouble remembering sight words and showing an inability to break words down into phonemes.

As a teacher you learn that you absolutely never label a child with a diagnosis, even if you think you see clear signs that something is amiss. Instead you begin a dialog with the parents to see if they too are seeing the developmental delays and then, after a few conversations, you refer them to a professional who will do a number of tests before making a diagnosis. I loved brainstorming ways to help my struggling students and found that I was particularly interested in students I thought had characteristics of dyslexia. Even though I strived to give as much attention to each and every student, I gave my struggling students more time and extra encouragement.

I will admit that the rules of grammar still don't always make sense to me and that before getting in front of the students to teach a reading or writing lesson, I always practiced to make sure I absolutely understood a concept. I often consulted colleagues to make sure I was on point or to ask ways to better explain a grammatical concept. I never once gave a Language Arts lesson that I had not thought about and reviewed multiple times—I just knew that I couldn't do it on the fly. I found I had to know the topic cold, including having some example to prove the rule, if I was going to be able to effectively teach the lesson. For example, when I did a lesson on the vowel team "oa" I made sure I could properly pronounce the combination, knew words that fit the rule as well as knew words where "o" and "a" together made a different sound. On the flip side, with math lessons, I could teach the concept and as I was giving the lesson I could improvise and add additional examples if I thought my students needed it. I was even able to develop strong add on lessons and create games to strengthen skills.

I had one student in particular when I was teaching first grade that I really identified with because of her struggles learning to read and write. She was a very bright, outgoing and creative girl. She had lots of friends and seemed happy most of the day. When she spoke, she made excellent observations and had many good insights. When it came time to learn how to read, however, I noticed that she might know a word on one page, but then three pages later have no idea how to pronounce the same word. She had a very hard time sounding out words or seeing any patterns in the language. She always used the pictures to figure out words in books and many times the words she said were not even close to the words written on the page— they even started with different letters. When it came to writing, she would tell me these incredible stories, but then forget them as she tried to figure out what letters to use to write down her words. She had a hard time incorporating sight words into her writing and often skipped words so that the sentences did not make sense unless you had been there while she was writing the piece. I spent a good deal of time working with her one on one throughout the year. In reading we reviewed sight words and tried to find patterns. We worked on using clues, such as the first letter, to help figure out the word. In writing, I would have her tell me her thoughts and I would repeat them back to her so she wouldn't forget them as she tried to write them out. When we worked together I would have her focus on one thing at a time instead of trying to make everything perfect. For instance, for one writing lesson I might have her think about remembering just a few sight words, such as "the" or "and" instead of all of the sight words we had learned. Once she felt solid on "the" and "and' we would incorporate a new word.

There were times when I became frustrated because she was so inconsistent—one day she would know a word well and then the next day have no idea what it could be. I think part of the frustration I felt was that I couldn't help her more. Whenever I felt myself becoming impatient, I would take a break, work with another student, and then go back to check in with her. I never wanted her to feel that I was in any way annoyed with her.

One important thing I realized from my time in the classroom is that each child is absolutely amazing in some way. Some kids made it easier to find that incredible thing, while with others you had to search a bit more. I started taking graduate courses in education at night and loved using what I had learned in my courses in the classroom.

San Francisco

In April of 2006, my boyfriend of a year was offered a position at an educational non-profit based in San Francisco. It was an incredible career opportunity for him and he wanted to take it, but only if I agreed to go with him. Change is challenging for me, especially since I had finally reached a comfortable place in my life: I loved my apartment and my job, I had my family nearby and I had a great circle of friends. On the other hand, I had also always loved San Francisco and had dreamed of living there at some point in my life. Additionally, my relationship was getting serious, but I had a number of nagging misgivings, and I wanted the opportunity to see more clearly if he was "the one." I figured that I would know for sure once we were away from our families and friends and it was just the two of us.

So, I packed up my apartment and we hit the road at the end of June in 2006. I had been so busy finishing the school year and writing my thesis for my Masters in Education that I left New York without having a job waiting for me in San Francisco. My school paid on a year-round schedule, meaning I would be paid through August, so I figured I had until August to land my next job. I had also been thinking a lot about writing a book about my experiences with dyslexia and reckoned the interim between our arrival and me finding a job would be the perfect time to do some writing because the time just felt right to start getting my ideas onto paper.

Before we left, I started a blog. My blog had two purposes. The first was to keep my family up to date on what I was up to, and thus avoid endless "checking in" phone calls, and the second was for me to start writing. Although I had written many papers in graduate school, I did not have a lot of experience writing biographical and/or non-academic pieces. My first entries were about the arduous task of packing up the apartment, followed by descriptions of places we stopped while driving cross-country. As I started to loosen up a bit, I begin writing about humorous run-ins and my thoughts on different environmental issues. My daily entries allowed me to start expressing myself without too much pressure. I am certain my daily writings helped me to get started on this project.

I had not given enough thought to how hard it was going to be for me to find that job. I know I could have been a substitute teacher or even tried to get a last minute teaching position, but I also had in my mind that I wanted to explore another area: the intersection between good business strategies and environmentally sustainable practices. I was close to being finished with a certificate in Conservation Biology from the Center for Environmental Research and Conservation at Columbia University. I had been completing the coursework at night. I figured that if I were going to ever try out environmental business, San Francisco would be the place to do it.

After a month of apartment hunting and frantic writing (many times it felt as though I could not write fast enough), I started to search the Internet for job postings. I came upon a few interesting ones and began to compose my cover letters. Writing a cover letter is an extremely laborious and anxiety-provoking process for me. Just sitting down to start a letter makes me incredibly edgy. It takes me a full day and usually a few bouts of tears to write one cover letter because I write, re-write and then re-word every sentence endlessly. It was an exhausting process. In the beginning, I was determined to do it by myself. I figured that by this point in my life, and with a Masters degree behind me that I could handle a few cover letters. However, as the search continued with little success, I started to get a bit crazed. I finally broke down one day and asked my boyfriend to look over two of the cover letters I had been belaboring. He said they were okay, but that they needed some work and that he would edit them for me. I was briefly relieved to have them out of my hands. A day passed, then another. I inquired over the letters. He said he was working on them, but needed time, so I did not push it. A few days after that, he returned them to me. They letters were nothing like the ones I had showed him. True, they were much better, but the letters were no longer in my words. I know he thought he had done me a huge favor, but it upset me. I felt as though I was back in high school and my brother was helping me with my college essays. Secondly, I thought that he had taken an unnecessarily long time with the cover letters. In addition, by completely re-writing them, it was as though he was saying my writing was no good and that if I really wanted to get a job, I would need his help to do it. It seemed to me that he wanted to take one of my weaknesses and use it to his advantage by making me dependent on him. Whether or not that was his intention, I was crushed, but also desperate. I ended up using one of the letters. The cover letter, a few writing samples and my resume got me an interview, a second interview and then a job.

What I had not realized was that the job would be writing-heavy. In fact, the job required constant report writing. I worked closely with a senior project manager who found many faults with my writing. She pointed out that I used the passive voice too often, had way too many sentence fragments and sprinkled commas like confetti. She suggested a business-writing course.

What I realized from the whole experience was that I had un-learned an important lesson: I had to do things for myself for me to feel confident in my abilities. If I "cheated" in any way, it would undermine my self-esteem. I got my foot in the door at the company because of my stellar cover letter, but it had misrepresented my abilities.

After a few months in San Francisco with my boyfriend, I knew that he was not "the one." It was a combination of things, but the incident with the cover letters really sealed the deal. Something my mother said has always resonated with me. She said that my father has never pointed out or focused on her weaknesses, instead he has been the ultimate cheerleader, pushing her to realize her aspirations. I know more clearly now that I need a mate who sees my strengths and does not focus on or use my weaknesses against me.

Business School

I don't remember exactly when it started, but my father and I have been talking about money for a very long time. I was always interested in how money was made and how to save it for the future. One of my favorite things to do as a child was to go to the bank and deposit money in my account. I was always saving for something big—what it was I didn't know. I just knew I loved saving. I have my old bankbook with deposits ranging from $3.23 to $6.72.

Although I became a teacher after college, I still thought about business, especially in the context of non-profits. The summer of 2007 I decided it was time for me to try to go to business school even though I did not have a background in anything specifically related to business. I only found one school I wanted to go to because I wanted to stay in New York City and continue to work full-time. The thought of not working, while racking up huge debt, was just too scary.

I attacked the application process as I had learned to go after the things I really wanted. I started early, made a detailed game plan, and then went about methodically working on it. First was the GMAT. Unlike my brother who took the test one day on a whim and did really well, I knew I needed to take a course, so I would know what to expect and how to approach the reading comprehension. I studied every night for a few months and it paid off.

The application required a few essays. I started right away so I would have time to think about them. I brainstormed on the bus, in bed at night and with friends who knew me well. I had to get across very clearly why I thought I absolutely needed a business degree, how NYU Stern was the best fit for me and how I was unique and would add something to their program. I also employed a friend, Deb, who I knew was an excellent writer, had been to business school and had a very sharp, analytical mind. When I approached her about helping me, I made it very clear that I was going to write all the essays and that I just needed very pointed feedback. We made a plan to meet every two or three weeks. Unlike my ex-boyfriend who took days to proof cover letters and then handed them back completely reworked, Deb was very respectful of my work. She never tried to write the essays, she just asked a lot of questions and told me what she thought my essays were saying to the reader. When I was stuck she would ask me to talk out loud, as Esther had done in college, and would write down my words. Often times I ended up using sentences in my essays that I had said aloud. It was an amazing working relationship for me because I not only produced a good finished product, but I also learned how to be a better writer in the process.

I went into the process of applying to business school very aware of my strengths and weaknesses and was able to find the help I needed, a GMAT course and a friend who could gave excellent feedback, to get the result I wanted.

*   *   *

I have really enjoyed the coursework in business school. Before I started, I briefly debated letting the Center for Students with Disabilities know about my dyslexia. Although it feels as though I have come a long way and that dyslexia is not a major obstacle in my life at this point, I wondered whether business school might be really challenging and if I would come up against any walls. And if I did, it would be good to have my diagnosis on record, so it wouldn't seem like an excuse. On the other hand, I also wanted to see how things would go without letting anyone know and I had done fine getting my Masters in Education. Just as my parents hadn't told Chapin, part of me wanted to wait and see how I handled the new expectations.

My first semester, I really hit the books and studied hard, while making it a point to be at most of the happy hours and school events. To say I was a busy semester working full-time and going to school at night while going to almost every social event they had would be an understatement. Luckily, I had already taken a statistics course and loved it and my other course was in Leadership, which I found very interesting. I got a 4.0 my first semester, which was a huge boost. Being one of the only teachers in business school, I had worried that I did not have a strong enough background and that I would not be able to keep up. Getting good grades right off the bat put me at ease that I could not only get into business school, but I could also do well.

Chapter 8

The Journey Continues
(Christine)

Although I have always thought of myself as an involved and focused parent, reading what Catherine has written here has definitely given me reason for pause. It strikes me how little we all know our own children. I was not totally aware of her reality, particularly as a young child, until I read her book. Her perceptual confusion and her frustration and anger were largely lost in the shuffle of a very busy life. Her personal coping skills in retrospect saved her from becoming another "bad" student. Even though there were guides, tutors, and coaches along the way, Catherine was the truly the master of her own educational destiny. Not every child with dyslexia will be as determined or fortunate as she has been.

Catherine has made a conscious choice to be an advocate. This book was written to give others, children and parents alike, a perspective on dyslexia. Catherine wrote it from the inside out, looking backwards at the struggle and moving forward with practical suggestions for how to create a successful and satisfying life in spite of the disability. Catherine has always been a very private and humble person and the fact that she would spend a year of her life writing this book, risking exposure of herself in a public way, speaks volumes. She never identified herself, save for the Latin fiasco, as a person with dyslexia. Most of her close friends were not aware of this issue until she began to write this book. She is a kind and gentle woman and I think that as she began to teach young children, she became acutely aware that many with this problem would not fare as well as she had without early and targeted intervention. Catherine identified with her students who were struggling and she felt that she needed to give these children words and thus a voice.

Catherine's life journey with dyslexia, has taken us all down a long and winding road. There have been potholes, (English grammar) and there have been virtual roadblocks, (Latin), along the way. There have been treacherous abyss' to climb out of, (serious depression), and there have been glorious days standing on the mountaintop, (Catherine's many, many successes). As I have now come to understand, the journey continues through life. Through intelligence, tenacity and determination, Catherine has learned how to package her disability into manageable luggage, rather than hopeless baggage, and she has set for herself very ambitious and worldly goals, which I am sure she will attain.

Today

(Catherine)

After all the writing I have done, it still surprises me that I decided to undertake this project. Even five years ago, I would never have dreamed that I would willingly take on a task that involved such extensive writing about such a personal topic. It has been an emotional journey.

What has kept me going when I was frustrated and feeling intense self-doubt was the thought that I am doing something that might help another person. So there are a few grammatical errors and misspelled words, does that really matter if there is a mother who reads this book, after learning her child's diagnosis, and finds comfort in my words?

I often wonder if I had not been dyslexic, would I really understand how difficult it is to have a learning disability? I wonder if I, as a teacher, might have been similarly insensitive to struggling students had I not felt such potent frustration as a student. It is so easy to assume a student is not trying hard enough when they do not seem to ascertain fairly basic skills like spelling and grammar. It is much more difficult to pinpoint the specific things a student is struggling with, the possible reasons why and then come up with helpful modifications. Sure, there are some students do not apply themselves, but I am willing to bet that many students who do not appear to be trying, especially in the lower grades, are frustrated or have had negative academic experiences in the past. I believe that my experience with dyslexia has made me a much kinder person. I can feel the pain and frustration of other people fairly easily. It hurts me to see others thwarted and upset.

I recognize that effort is not manifest in the product. One person's easy accomplishment might mean a heroic effort by another. Victory lies in the space between where a student was and where they stretched themselves to get to, even if it appears negligible. It is so easy to praise the student who consistently writes well thought-out and organized papers. It is much harder, but so important, to praise incremental changes in the student who is struggling to achieve at all.

As a teacher, I found myself radiating towards students who expressed frustration or difficulty in an area of their learning. I wanted more than anything to figure out what exactly they did not understand and how I could help them grasp the allusive concept. It was a challenge to come up with different ways of explaining the same thing. I also tutored math for a middle school student in the evenings and loved explaining geometry and algebra in multiple ways. One of the huge advantages of working in a small private school is that I can spend one-on-one time with each of my students. I hope my attention to each of their learning styles helped them to not only learn, but to enjoy school.

In my bi-yearly conferences with parents, I am always honest. It is tempting to gloss over a child's difficulties and only mention their strengths. Especially with really young children, parents are very resistant to hearing that their angel isn't "perfect". Teachers have a unique perspective on child development because they see each child in relation to the group. Although they do not compare the children to each other, they can notice when a child is lagging behind her peers in a particular area. As discussed earlier, in the preschool classroom, indicators such as word mispronunciations, difficulty sequencing, not understanding the concept of rhyming and poor letter recognition (after significant exposure) can be indicators of potential problems. Although it may make a parent unhappy to hear that their child is not the best at everything, it might help them to get their child assistance, if it is needed, and avoid future struggles.

It makes me angry to think of how many children go through the educational system, public, private and parochial, without being identified as needing help. It amazes me that my own school never identified that something was amiss. It took my mother's sense that something was wrong and her incredible persistence, for me to get help.

I still experience bouts of anxiety. Whether I am genetically predisposed to experiencing anxiety or it is a by-product of my academic struggles, I do not know. Certain situations are particularly anxiety producing. Any kind of move or change is hard for me. Not until I have been somewhere or have done a job for a while do I feel comfortable.

I have actively been working on reducing my anxiety. I go to yoga class, try to meditate and exercise regularly. Sewing and knitting while watching television is relaxing after a long interactive day teaching. I also try to get a good night's sleep and rarely drink more than one cup of coffee a day.

I have also made a big effort to congratulate myself on the things I have accomplished. It is so easy to look ahead and become overwhelmed by the challenges. I keep lists in the back of my journal of things I have done or am good at doing. Every once in a while after a bad day, I will re-read some of the entries to remind myself of all that I have done. Although I am actively working on it, my stress level still spikes at times. When this happens, I rely on my friends and family for support. I have an incredible network of people whom I love and who support me when I doubt myself.

I completed a graduate degree in Early Childhood Education in 2006. I really enjoyed being in graduate school and learning about education while I was teaching. My program was very comprehensive. I took courses in the history of education, major educational philosophers, child development, language acquisition, setting up a classroom, early math, reading and writing, and curriculum development. Autism is a hot topic right now, and it was discussed in many of my courses. Interestingly though, there was little mention of dyslexia or other reading-related problems. The program had so many areas to cover, I know there was just not enough time to focus on everything, but I believe that dyslexia is such a prevalent disorder that it needs more time in the graduate school curriculum. Early childhood is the best time for remediation, so we need to train our early childhood educators to recognize the early signs of dyslexia. As a result, one of my goals for the future is to bring more awareness of reading-related disabilities to early childhood teacher education programs.

Having done the research for this book, I am more aware of some of the symptoms I still have. Thank goodness for my computer's spell and grammar check, because I continue to have a lot of trouble spelling and making complete sentences. I notice in conversation that I am sometimes slow to retrieve words. I will know that there is a specific word I want to use, but will not be able to think of it. Mostly, in those situations, I will try to talk around the word or find a good substitute. I also continue to have poor balance. I find myself off-kilter regularly and have to hold onto large objects to steady myself. Overall, I find that these areas of weakness are greatly overshadowed by what I consider to be my strengths. I am a compassionate, thoughtful and intelligent person. I absolutely love to learn and am always reading.

Advice

One of the reasons I undertook writing this book was to share my journey with other dyslexics, parents of dyslexics and teachers. My hope is that by sharing my story, it might make the ride a little smoother for others. I was once asked what advice I would give to other families or people struggling with dyslexia.

Some things I would suggest for dyslexic individuals:

- Be creative.
- Nothing happens overnight—be patient.
- Know yourself and how you learn best. If you need to have absolute quiet to concentrate, find quiet places to work or get really good earplugs.
- Play to your strengths—if you are your most creative when you are brainstorming, find people to brainstorm with before starting a project.

- Develop other areas of strength. Having outlets is important and it builds needed self-esteem.

- Create a strong support network of trusted family and friends with whom you can be honest and share your frustrations.

- Attack versus avoid, but know your limitations.

- Try crossword puzzles. Start with the easy ones and work your way up. I have found that the more crossword puzzles I do, the more I think about language and double meanings. They also force me to think about spelling.

- Keep a list of words you come across while reading that you do not know. Jot the words down, and then look them up later. Make flashcards and review them periodically.

- Check out books on tape from the library. If reading is laborious, listen to books. Do not miss out on the pleasure of literature.

- Keep a private journal and write all the time. Do not focus on spelling or grammar, just get writing.

- When you read, read high-quality literature so you can see what good writing looks and sounds like.

- Keep lists of your strengths to refer to when needed.

- Do some research on dyslexia and find a few good role models.

Some advice for parents:

- Be an advocate for your child—you know them best and if professionals don't agree that your child is struggling, seek another opinion.

- Be honest with your child and let them know that some things might be harder, but that you are going to work together as a team to figure them out.

- Only answer the questions they are asking about their learning problems—meaning that when they ask why things are hard for them, they might not be asking for the details of dyslexia, instead they might just need to know that everyone learns differently and that sometimes there is a little glitch that needs fixing.

- Address the issues, but do not make it the basis for your relationship—your child is so much more than a diagnosis.

- Find good role models and share them with your child—highlight that they might have had to work harder to learn, but that these accomplished people with the same learning problems, persevered and did incredible things.

- Encourage your child to explore their interests and find areas of strength outside of academics.

- Listen: sometimes all your child wants is for you to listen to them and to feel understood.

- Acknowledge their hard work and let them know that you see the effort that they are putting into learning. I know I loved hearing that my parents were proud of my efforts.

Appendices

Appendix A: Dyslexia in the United States

In the United States, it is estimated that between 5 and 17 percent of the population is dyslexic. Dyslexia is one of the most prevalent and studied learning differences. In fact, when I typed in "dyslexia" on PsychInfo, a searchable web database of psychology-related articles, 4529 hits came up for journal articles that mentioned dyslexia. Although schools tend to identify many more boys as having reading or pre-reading difficulties, Sally Shaywitz, co-director of the Yale Center for the Study of Learning and Attention, found that when tested, comparable numbers of boys and girls expressed dyslexic characteristics.[23]

---

[23] Sally Shaywitz (2003), <u>Overcoming Dyslexia</u>, Vintage Books; New York.

Appendix B: Defining Dyslexia

What exactly *is* dyslexia[24]? Although it seems a simple question, there is not a definitive answer in the form of a universally recognized definition for the disorder. In fact, experts continue to debate the specific criteria that constitute a diagnosis of dyslexia and thus what should be included in its definition. Having a universally recognized definition is important because it can be used to more clearly identify individuals with the disorder, and it can point to various areas for focused study as well as intervention strategies. There are a few widely used definitions of dyslexia. The one I feel captures it's essence the best:

> Dyslexia is a specific learning disability that is neurobiological in origin. It is characterized by difficulties with accurate and/or fluent word recognition and by poor spelling and decoding abilities. These difficulties typically result from a deficit in the phonological component of language that is often unexpected in relation to other cognitive abilities and the provision of effective classroom instruction. Secondary consequences include problems in reading comprehension and reduced reading experience that can

---

[24] In an effort to be as clear as possible, in this book we will be using the term dyslexia in the place of developmental dyslexia and/or specific reading disability.

impede growth of vocabulary and background knowledge.[25]

Although this definition is robust and includes some of the deficits and difficulties associated with dyslexia, it does not specify whether the neurobiological component is the result of genetics, environmental influences or a combination of the two. As research progresses and we get a better understanding of dyslexia, a newer, more precise definition will likely emerge. Until then, I believe the above is a good starting point.

---

[25] Adopted by the International Dyslexia Association Board of Directors on November 12, 2002.

Appendix C: Difficulties Associated with Dyslexia

Dyslexic individuals vary widely in their profiles of abilities and deficits across reading-related measures. Below is a chart of the most common deficiencies associated with the disorder. The double asterisks (**) indicate a characteristic of most people identified as dyslexic.

Delayed Speech	Slow acquisition of spoken language.
Weak Phonological Awareness**	Phonological awareness refers to the earlier stages of developing the awareness of different sound units, including small units (phonemes) and larger units such as beginning sounds (onsets) and rhymes. This also includes trouble learning and remembering letter sounds (sound-symbol correspondence).
Weak Phonemic Awareness**	Phonemic awareness is a more advanced understanding of the parts of words. It encompasses the ability to not only notice, but also identify and

	manipulate the smallest parts that make up a word. This skill is also known as decoding, or breaking the word down to figure it out.
Weak Phonological Processing**	Slow or inaccurate decoding of the units of language to produce meaningful words.
Poor Working (Short-term) Memory**	Difficulty recalling a series of phonemes or numbers immediately following their presentation.
Poor Auditory Discrimination**	Auditory discrimination is the awareness of the segments of speech and the ability to dissect words into phonemes and manipulate them.
Perceptual Reversals in Reading and Writing	Most children reverse letters when they are learning to write. A dyslexic child may continue to do this after peers have moved on. This is not a key component of the disorder.
Impaired Reproduction of Rhythmic Patterns**	When presented with a word, a child will have difficulty identifying an appropriate word that rhymes with it.
Impaired Reproduction of	Trouble reproducing patterns presented tonally, this relates

Tonal Patterns**	to poor working memory.
Faulty Auditory Sequencing	Trouble repeating back the details of a story in the correct sequence.
Speech Irregularities	Slurred words, mispronunciations, word repetitions, noticeable hesitation and incomplete sentences (beyond appropriate ages).
Difficulty with Verbal Expression	Unclear speech and slow processing during a conversation.
Delayed Word Retrieval (Slow Automatic Naming)	Unusually long times needed to produce specific words. People who have trouble retrieving words will often explain what they are trying to say using other words.
Impaired Right-Left Discrimination	Trouble identifying which direction is right and which is left.
Impaired Coordination	Non-specific motor awkwardness.
Trouble Memorizing Number Facts	Difficulty memorizing properties of numbers.
Difficulty Follow Math Procedures	Confusion over which steps to take and in what order.

Spelling Difficulties	Repeated mistakes and difficulty applying learned spelling rules. This includes even simple words.
Small Sight Word Vocabulary	Few words are automatically recognized, even with significant exposure to print.
Disorganized Written and Spoken Language	A student will have good ideas, but trouble ordering and presenting them in a logical fashion.
Syntax Confusion	Difficulty remembering and applying grammatical rules related to sentence structure.

Appendix D: Signs of Learning Differences Beginning at Birth

In recent years, there has been a big push to conclusively identify the early warning signs of dyslexia. A number of excellent longitudinal (long-term) studies are being conducted that compare at-risk children (having one parent and one first degree relative with dyslexia) with control children (no reported history of reading problems in the family). Past studies have shown that a parent with dyslexia has a roughly 50% chance of having a child with dyslexia.

The Jyvaskyla Longitudinal Study of Dyslexia (JLD), which is run through the Department of Child Psychology and the Child Research Centre at the University of Jyvaskyla in Finland, has followed a group of Finnish children since birth. They split the group into children at risk for familial dyslexia (n=107) and controls (n=93). By studying these children starting at birth, the JLD researchers hoped to observe familial/genetic influences before the children are exposed to environmental factors that could help them compensate for any deficiencies. The JLD has continued to publish their findings as the children have aged.

The JLD researchers found that the at-risk and control children did not differ at birth in gestational age, birth weight or Apgar scores (a test done right after birth to determine the healthiness of an infant).

At six months, the researchers administered a test to look at the infants' response to similar-sounding speech sounds and the time it took them to discriminate between the two sounds.

The researchers found that the at-risk infants required a longer duration to discriminate between two similar sounds. Interestingly, the researchers administered the same test to the parents of the study participants. The parents identified as dyslexic showed the same subtle differences in categorical discrimination as compared to the control group parents. The results point to auditory perception as an important precursor for later reading development.

In another test, the researchers asked parents to record their infants' early vocalizations as well as fine and gross motor development. No differences were found between the at-risk and control infants. However, the at-risk infants with markedly slow motor development also had a smaller vocabulary and used shorter sentences later on. One of the most significant findings for the at-risk group (this does not apply to the control group) was that almost every child that had delayed speech subsequently experienced significant trouble learning to read.

Viewed in isolation, these findings do not reveal a huge amount, however, when pieced together, they form a good set of clues concerning later reading development.

Appendix E: Eyesight and Dyslexia

Although some people have wondered whether reading acquisition is connected to the process of seeing, Pediatric Ophthalmologist Norman Medow has found that learning disabilities are most often not related to vision problems. Vision might play a role in perception, but it does not account for the deeper issues, such as phonemic awareness, in reading acquisition. No scientific evidence has shown that visual training, muscle, perceptual or hand/eye coordination exercises can improve a child's learning disability.[26] To further prove the point that dyslexia is not a vision problem, there are dyslexic Braille readers.[27]

---

[26] Learning disabilities pamphlet produced by the American Academy of Ophthalmology.

[27] Charters, L. (2006) Children's reading problems can be complicated to decipher. Ophthalmology Times Sept. 15, 2006.

Appendix F: Early Childhood Indicators of Later Reading Difficulty

Delays in speech and language including articulation errors that persist past the point where they are age-appropriate can be a warning sign of later learning issues. Articulation errors can disappear as a child's mouth matures and some parents prefer to wait and see if the child grows out of it, but as a teacher, I believe it is better to have things checked out sooner rather than later. In addition to correcting mispronunciations, speech therapy can also be the first step to identification of larger language or processing problems.

Additionally, for children ages three to five, delays in co-ordination, attention, practical language, sequencing and perception are further indicators that the child may develop later reading difficulties.[28] Examples include the four year old who has been exposed to a significant amount of print, but cannot seem to learn some of the letter names or sounds. Or the child that appears clumsy, bumping into people and objects frequently. This can also mean a child who seems to have difficulty processing language and responding appropriately; such as a delayed response to a question or directions or a response that does not fit with the question asked. Children who have trouble with word retrieval (quickly naming familiar objects) also show increased risk for later learning disabilities.

---

[28] J.S. Pickering

Another clue that a child might develop subsequent reading problems is if they have difficulty repeating back a sequence of events in the correct order. This might include a child who has heard a story read aloud, but when asked to retell it, although he/she may know a number of the details, has trouble with the story's sequence. The retelling thus seems almost haphazard.

Another big indicator in preschool that a child might develop later difficulties reading is weak phonological awareness. Phonological awareness refers to the awareness of different sound units. Phonological awareness encompasses the ability to learn letter sounds and take note of onsets (the beginning sound in a word) and rhymes. A child who has low phonological awareness might have difficulty rhyming because he is unable to isolate the last part of the word and make sure the sound corresponds to the ending sound of another word.

Although long touted as the telltale sign of dyslexia, mirror reading and writing is in fact not common to all dyslexics nor are children who write backwards necessarily dyslexic. It is very common for young children, four to six, to confuse letter directionality. Furthermore, until a child grasps that words are the synthesis of many symbols placed in a specific order, it does not matter to the child how the word is constructed. A name front-wards and backwards is still the name because it contains all of the necessary letters.

Early childhood lays the foundation for later academic work, so if there are areas of uneven growth, it is important to recognize them. With students who have a high genetic risk for being dyslexic, it is especially important that these first signs of difficulty not be ignored. Continued assessment of a child's progress in rhyming, letter-sound correspondence and automatic naming can also help identify whether a child is progressing appropriately or if they are stuck.

Appendix G: Phonemic Awareness and Reading

Much of early elementary school focuses on reading acquisition in the form of phonemic awareness. Phonemic awareness is a more advanced understanding of the parts that make up a word and the ability to segment and manipulate those parts to either read or write an unfamiliar word. The ability to recognize and properly manipulate segments of words is also referred to as decoding. Difficulty decoding is one of the cruxes of dyslexia. A dyslexic student might be able to "read" a difficult word because they have seen it before, but when they are asked to separate it into segments and then substitute a segment, they are lost. For example, when asked, they will have difficulty separating the word hopefully into it's segments, hope-ful-ly and even greater trouble if they are then asked to change that word to hopelessly which requires substituting -ful with -less in the middle of the word.

Another clue that a child might be dyslexic is an uneven academic profile. The child might appear to be bright and performing well overall, but standardized testing may reveal one or two areas that are in a much lower range than of the other scores. An uneven profile is a major red flag that the student has very specific deficiencies that need attention.

Appendix H: Genetics and Dyslexia

Researchers have found that children with dyslexia often times have a close relative, diagnosed or not, who displays dyslexic characteristics. Conversely, a parent with dyslexia has a fifty percent chance of passing the disorder on to each of their offspring. Clyde Francks et al (2002) found strong results that indicate genetic linkages on chromosome loci 6 and 18. Other researchers have pinpointed further possible candidate genes. Although it has been narrowed down, there are still tens of hundred of candidate genes that could all contribute to the expression of dyslexia. While researchers may not know conclusively which genes are responsible for dyslexia, they are sure that there is a strong genetic component involved.

As with many genetic studies, work with identical and fraternal twins is especially illuminating. Defries & Gillis (1993) found that for monozygotic (identical) twins, in 66% of pairs, both children had dyslexia, while for dizygotic (fraternal) twins only 43% of both the children had dyslexia. This indicates not only a strong genetic component, but also highlights the fact that dyslexia is not entirely a function of a person's genetic make-up: how dyslexia is expressed is influenced by the child's environment.

Appendix I: The Dyslexic Brain

It is clear that the brain of a dyslexic individual functions differently than the brain of a non-impaired person. Exciting research is being done with functional magnetic resonance imaging (fMRIs) that has shed light on how the dyslexic's brain functions differently than a "normal" brain when engaged in literacy tasks. (Shaywitz & Shaywitz, 2003) These non-invasive brain scans work by detecting changes in oxygenated blood flow as a result of metabolic activity to specific areas of the brain (because as an area of the brain is activated, more metabolic activity takes place and thus more oxygen is required to complete the task, which in turn produces a stronger magnetic signal) after stimuli is presented. For instance, if a person is asked to read a passage, the fMRI will show what parts of the brain are used to perform this task. The more heavily a brain area is used, the brighter the corresponding image will be on the fMRI scan.

From past research and these incredible scans, we now know that for most unimpaired people, the left hemisphere of the brain is most heavily activated during reading activities. There are three specific regions that have been identified as playing a role in reading:

Neural Systems for Reading

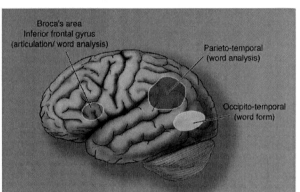

© Sally Shaywitz, *Overcoming Dyslexia*, 2003

1. **Left Inferior Frontal Gyrus** (Phoneme Producer) This area of the brain initiates the analysis of phonemes (sound units) and helps a person vocalize words silently or aloud. This area is very active when a person is beginning to learn how to read.

2. **Left Parieto-Temporal Area** (Word Analyzer) This part of the brain assists with a more complete analysis of the word. This area of the brain can pull apart words making them into syllables. On fMRI's, this area of the brain showed diminished activation among skilled readers.

3. **Left Occipito-Temporal Area** (Automatic Detector) When reading, this part of the brain facilitates the automatic recognition of words. The more often this area is activated, the more proficient it becomes, thus helping the reader process text faster. Reading skill has been

positively correlated with the degree of activation observed in this region. [29]

As opposed to their peers, dyslexics appear to lean heavily on the Left Inferior Frontal Gyrus and areas in the right lobe when engaged in literacy activities. These findings suggest that people with dyslexia compensate for diminished activation of the more sophisticated areas of the brain by activating compensatory brain systems, such as using visual clues, when trying to read.

Although initially a dyslexic's brain may function differently, Shaywitz & Shaywitz (2005) found that after targeted remediation, dyslexics do activate areas of their brain that were not used previously when reading. That indicates both a high plasticity of the brain, and that the neural pathways in the brain are able to change as a result of targeted intervention.

---

[29] Diane J. Sawyer. <u>Dyslexia: A Generation of Inquiry.</u> Topics in Language Disorders. Vol. 26(2) April/June 2006, pp 95-109.

Appendix J: Typical Assessment Components

Formal evaluations are prepared by highly trained educational psychologists and can be undertaken at a city/county facility or privately. An evaluation is necessary to determine whether a person has dyslexia.[30] The assessment aims to ascertain general intellectual abilities, information processing skills, and psycholinguistic processing competencies. The chart below highlights specific subtests that are typically included, depending upon the age of the subject, in a formal evaluation.

Phonological and Phonemic Awareness	These tests will typical ask the student to orally manipulate the sounds in a presented word. These might include having students indicate similarities or differences among words on the basis of their first, last or middle sounds, or telling how many different sounds a word contains or blending two separately presented sounds to make a word.
Phonemic Decoding Efficiency	Reading printed nonsense words aloud. This test not only looks at the accuracy, but at the time it

---

[30] Almost all states require a formal assessment to determine which services a student is entitled to receive.

	takes to make the utterance.
Orthographic Coding	Orthographic patterns are patterns of letter combinations that frequently occur in words. This is assessed along with phonemic decoding to see whether the student recognizes common letter groupings and the sounds they will make.
Word Recognition	Unrelated words of increasing difficulty are shown to students to read aloud until there is an error. This assesses sight word recognition and the student's ability to figure out unknown words.
Rapid Automatic Naming	Students rapidly name visually presented stimulus (letters, digits, objects, numbers). This test assesses the student's ability to retrieve words from memory.
Spelling (Visual Memory)	Students will be asked to either write a short piece or they will be asked to write out a list of words given orally.
Verbal Short-term memory	Students are asked to repeat single non-words that vary in length from 2 or 3 phonemes to 8 or 10 phonemes. Similar tests are also given using numbers.

Depending on how old the child is when she/he is referred for testing, different tests are administered.

Typically, pre-kindergarten students (four to five years) take phonological awareness and rapid automatic naming tests. They may also undertake a verbal short-term memory test. The verbal short-term memory test is not usually given if the two prior tests are administered.

In early kindergarten (around five years of age), the above tests are given in addition to an assessment of letter-name knowledge. By late kindergarten, students are also assessed for their knowledge of letter sounds.

If students are assessed at the end of first grade, tests of phonemic decoding efficiency are given because at this age, they are more predictive of dyslexia than either phonemic awareness or rapid automatic naming tests. Students will also take orthographic coding and word recognition tests.

Although less commonly used than ten years ago, some evaluators use IQ tests as another tool for getting a fuller understanding of a student's strengths and weaknesses. In the past, one of the criteria for a dyslexia diagnosis was a marked difference between the student's IQ score, hence "intelligence", and how she/he was performing in the classroom. It was believed that dyslexics were of average to high intelligence, but got marks in school that did not reflect their inherent "intelligence."

As students age past second grade, they are assessed on a combination of tasks: rapid automatic naming, phonemic decoding efficiency, orthographic decoding, word recognition, spelling, verbal short-term memory and written expression.

Appendix K: Third Grade

Third Grade seems to be an important time for diagnosis, because the dyslexic's difficulties are more pronounced. While able readers continue to make progress, the struggling reader is still trying to tackle the more basic aspects of reading. Two obvious difficulties are present when the struggling reader is asked to read at their grade level; first, he/she will recognize fewer "sight words", words that do not need to be sounded out because the meaning is immediately known, than her peers.[31] And secondly his/her attempts to identify words will produce numerous errors. When reading aloud, students with reading issues will "miss more short words than long words, which are more distinctly different from one another."[32] In other words, when reading a passage, a child might incorrectly read easy words such as "the" or "and" as something else. The same student will likely also make many guesses, some of which seem incredibly random, when presented with an unknown word. These students will not successfully use letter-sound relationships (phonics) in combination with contextual clues to identify unknown words. "Because the broad verbal abilities of these children are substantially higher than their reading abilities, usually, the word reading difficulties of these children

---

[31] C. Schatschneider & T. Torgesen, (2004) Using Our Current Understanding of Dyslexia to Support Early identification and Intervention Journal *of Child Neurology* vol. 19, Number 10, pg. 759)

[32] Pickering pg 46.

present the most immediate barrier to good reading comprehension."[33]

This is the time when the struggling student will become more confused and frustrated. It is important to note that although adults may assume that a student is not motivated if their grades and not as good as expected, "motivation is rarely, if ever, the cause of reading failure."[34] Everyone wants to know how to read. Our culture is based on the ability to decipher the written word.

Students who experience continued frustration and confusion surrounding learning to read often exhibit emotional and behavioral overlays. Clowning, withdrawal and or hostility are all ways that a student might try to distract others from noticing his/her academic weaknesses. Reading out loud is a particular area of anxiety for the struggling reader. When it comes time to read aloud, the student who is aware that they cannot perform as well as peers will suddenly have to go to the bathroom or make a joke to divert attention away from their inability to read aloud fluently. Many struggling readers are finally identified as needing remediation in the Third Grade.

Reading aloud presents many challenges for the disabled reader. Note that "because words do not become 'sight words' until they are read accurately a number of times, inaccurate reading and diminished reading practice both cause slow growth in the number of words that can be recognized at a single glance."[35] Automatic and effortless identification of a

---

[33] Ibid, 760

[34] J.S. Pickering (2002) Signals of Learning Disabilities at Various Developmental Stages. *Montessori LIFE* pg. 48

[35] Schatschneider, 760.

large number of words is the most important factor in producing fluent reading. If a reader is constantly stopping to figure out a word, they loose the flow of the text and thus have a diminished comprehension of the passage as a whole.

Appendix L: The Dyslexic Child In Middle School

The dyslexic middle school child knows much more than they are able to effectively express in writing. The student will be able to tell the teacher all about a topic, but his written work will be awkward, disorganized, use simple short sentences and have repeated spelling and grammatical errors. During these years, issues of continued frustration and low self-esteem worsen. Pickering noted: "the more intellectually able the learning disabled student, the greater the frustration." A dyslexic child may appear angry or act out in unexpected ways during these years. He might also refer to himself as stupid and say that he is just not good at school. Often dyslexic children will resist going to school or even starting homework. When he is not at school, the dyslexic child will rarely read for pleasure.

Appendix M: Famous Dyslexics

I recently read Ronald Davis's book, <u>The Gift of Dyslexia</u>. I purchased the book because the title intrigued me. Although I had heard of many famous dyslexics, (in part because every time my mother read about one, she would clip out the article and give it to me), I had never thought of dyslexia as a gift. I figured that famous people who had it, achieved despite their learning disability. They were inherently talented enough that their reading difficulties did not hold them back. Davis disagrees. He posits that because dyslexics experience the world in a slightly altered way, they are uniquely equipped to be creative and see things that other people miss.

A 2003 article in The Sunday Times cited a study by Tulip Financial Research, which found that about 40% of the three hundred top business executives in Great Britain had been diagnosed with some sort of learning disability. The article goes on to speculate that the early frustrations probably added to more creative thinking and problem solving.

Here is a brief list (taken from a number of sources) of people thought to have dyslexia:

Performers/Actors

Whoopi Goldberg

Cher

Henry Winkler

Patrick Dempsey

Robin Williams

Jay Leno

River Phoenix

Harrison Ford

Orlando Bloom

Salma Hayek

John Lennon

Politicians

Gavin Newsom

Thomas Jefferson

John F. Kennedy

Winston Churchill

Nelson Rockefeller

George Washington

Artists

Walt Disney

Pablo Picasso

Leonardo Da Vinci

John Irving

Gustave Flaubert

Hans Christian Anderson

Richard Rogers (Arch.)

Lewis Carroll

Richard Ford

Steven Spielberg

Creative Thinkers/Inventors

Albert Einstein

Charles R. Schwab

Thomas Edison

Alexander Graham Bell

Henry Ford

Steve Jobs

Richard Branson

Athletes

Greg Louganis

Nolan Ryan

Mohammad Ali

Babe Ruth

Magic Johnson

Acknowledgements

A special thank you to my family for their love, support and understanding and especially my mother who agreed to take on this project because she knew how much it meant to me. Thank you to Ashar Choudhry for his unending encouragement. Thank you to Kate Johnson and Barbara Galletly at Georges Borchardt Agency for their patience and thoughtful edits. Thank you to my friends who have helped me to edit this manuscript along the way: Kimberly Palmer, Gavin Berger, Harold Evans, and Roberto Bailey. And last, but definitely not least, thank you to Patti Jo Lavallee for the fantastic cover design. I could not have made the idea for this book a reality without each and every one of you.

References

Alexander, AW & Slinger-Constant, AM. (2004) "Current Status of Treatments for Dyslexia: Critical Review." Journal of Child Neurology. October 2004, Vol. 19, Issue 10 pp 744-758.

American Academy of Ophthalmology. Learning disabilities pamphlet.

Boets, B., et al. (2006) "Auditory temporal information processing in preschool children at family risk for dyslexia: Relations with phonological abilities and developing literacy skills." Brain and Language 97 64-79.

Burden, R. (2005) Dyslexia and Self-Concept: Seeking a Dyslexic Identity. Philadelphia: Whurr Publishers.

Bruck, M. (1992) "Persistence of Dyslexics' Phonological Awareness Deficits." Developmental Psychology. Vol 28, No. 5 pp 874-886.

Carroll, JM & Iles, JE. (2006) "An Assessment of Anxiety Levels in Dyslexic Students in Higher Education." British Journal of Educational Psychology, Vol. 76, Number 3 pp.651-662.

Charters, L. (2006) "Children's Reading Problems Can be Complicated to Decipher." Ophthalmology Times. September 15, 2006.

Crombie, M.A. (1997) "The Effects of Specific Learning Difficulties (Dyslexia) on the Learning of a Foreign Language in School." Dyslexia Vol 3; 27-47.

Davis, Ronald, D. (1994) The Gift of Dyslexia: Why Some of the Smartest People Can't Read... and How They Can Learn. Perigee, New York.

DeFries, J.C., & Gillis, J.J. (1993) "Genetics of Reading Disability." In R. Plomin & G. McClearn (Eds.), Nature, nurture and psychology (pp. 121-145). Washington, DC: APA Press. *

Edwards, Janice. (1994) The Scars of Dyslexia. Cassell. New York.

Francks, C, et al. (2002) "The Genetic Basis of Dyslexia." Neurology Vol. 1 December. 483-90.

Gorman, C. (2003) "How the Brain Reads Words." Time 004-781X 7/28/2003 Vol. 162, Issue 4.

Hales, G (1994) "The Human Aspects of Dyslexia." In G. Hales (Ed.), Dyslexia Matters. London: Whurr. *

Koster, C et al. (2005) "Differences at 17 Months: Productive Language Patterns in Infants at Familial Risk for Dyslexia and Typically Developing Infants." Journal of Speech, Language, and Hearing Research. Vol. 48 pp. 426-438.

Kurnoff, Shirley. The Human Side of Dyslexia. London Universal, United States. July 2000 (e-book).*

As a mother with a dyslexic child, Kurnoff went looking for resources and found very little. This is an excellent book that looks at the emotional side of dyslexia within a family. The section of interviews with siblings of dyslexic students was especially informative.

Lyon G.R., Shaywitz S.E., Shaywitz B.A. (2003). "A Definition of Dyslexia." Annuls of Dyslexia; 53:1-14.

Lyytinen, H., et al. (2004) "The Development of Children at Familial Risk for Dyslexia: Birth to Early School Age." Annuls of Dyslexia Vol. 54, No. 2, pgs 184-220.

Lyytinen, H., et al. (2004) "Early Development of Children at Familial Risk for Dyslexia—Follow-up from Birth to School Age." Dyslexia 10;146-178.

Manis, FR, Doi, LM & Bhadha, B. (2000) "Naming Speed, Phonological Awareness, and Orthographic Knowledge in Second Graders." Journal of Learning Disabilities. July/August 33(4) pp 325-333.

Maughan, B. & Carroll B. (2006) "Literacy and Mental Disorders." Current Opinion in Psychiatry Vol. 19 pp 350-354.

Pickering, J.S. (2002) "Signals of Learning Disabilities at Various Developmental Stages." Montessori LIFE. Summer. pp 46-48.

Puolakanaho, A., et al. 92004) "Emerging Phonological Awareness Differentiates Children with and without Familial Risk for Dyslexia and Controlling for General Language Skills." Annals of Dyslexia, Vol. 54, No. 2. pp 221-245.

Riddick, B. (1996) Living with Dyslexia: The Social and Emotional Consequences of Specific Learning Difficulties. London: Routledge. *

Riddick, B, Sterling, C, Farmer, M & Morgan, S. (1999) "Self-Esteem and Anxiety in the Educational Histories of Adult Dyslexic Students." Dyslexia Vol. 5:227-248.

Royer, JM. (1997) "A Cognitive Perspective on the Assessment, Diagnosis, and Remediation of Reading Skills." Handbook of Academic Learning. pp 200-234.

Rutter, M & Maughan, B. "Dyslexia: 1965-2005." Behavioral and Cognitive Psychotherapy. October 2005, Vol. 33. Issue 4 p389-402.

Samuelsson, S., et al. (2003) "Reading and Writing Difficulties Among prison Inmates: A Matter of Experiential Factors Rather Than Dyslexic Problems." Scientific Studies of Reading, 7(1) pp 53-73.

Sawicki, Stephen. "Understanding Dyslexia." People 9/22/97 Vol. 48, Issue 12 p149 3p 5c.

Sayer, D. J. (2006) "Dyslexia: A Generation of Inquiry." Topics in Language Disorders. Vol. 26(2). April/June 2006, pp 95-109.

Selikowitz, M. Dyslexia: The Facts. Second Edition. Oxford, New York; 2003.

Schatschneider, C. & Togesen, J.K. (2004) "Using Our Current Understanding of Dyslexia to Support Early Identification and Intervention." Journal of Child Neurology, Vol. 19. Number 10, October 2004. pp 759-763

Shaywitz, S.E. & Shaywitz, B.A. (2005) "Dyslexia (Specific Reading Disability)" Biological Psychiatry 2005; 57: 1301-1309.

Shaywitz, S.E. & Shaywitz, B.A. (2004) "The New Science of Reading and its Implications for the Classroom. " Education Canada 44 no. 1, Winter 2004.

Shaywitz, S.E. & Shaywitz B.A. (2003) "Neurobiological Indices of Dyslexia." In H.L Swanson, K. R. Harris, & S.

Graham (Eds.), Handbook of Learning Disabilities (pp 514-531). New York: The Guilford Press.

Shaywitz, S.E. Overcoming Dyslexia: A New and Complete Science-Based Program for Reading Problems at Any Level. Vintage, New York: 2003.

Spreen, O. (1987) Learning Disabled Children Growing Up: a Follow Up Study into Adulthood. Lisse: Swets and Zeitlinger. *

The International Dyslexia Foundation Fact Sheet # 962-05/00, Fact Sheet #49-05/04: http://www.interdys.org

Vellutino, FR, Fletcher, JM, Snowling, MJ & Scanlon, DM. (2004) "Specific Reading Disability (Dyslexia): What Have We Learned in the Past Four Decades?" Journal of Child Psychology and Psychiatry. 45:1 pp 2-40.

Wagner, RK, Francis, DJ & Morris, RD. (2005) "Identifying English Language Learners with Learning Disabilities: Key Challenges and Possible Approaches." Learning Disabilities Research & Practice. 20(1) pp 6-15.

Weinstein, L. Reading David: A Mother and Son's Journey through the Labrinth of Dyslexia. Perigee, New York; 2003.

Suggested Websites

International Dyslexia Association: http://www.interdys.org/

The Yale Center for Dyslexia and Creativity:
http://dyslexia.yale.edu/index.html

Mayo Clinic Website on Dyslexia:
http://www.mayoclinic.com/health/dyslexia/DS00224

Child Mind Institute: http://www.childmind.org/

I would love to hear from you!

Follow my blog: http://backwordsforword.blogspot.com/
Contact me at catherinehirschman@yahoo.com

The Authors

Christine Melton, MD, MS, is an Ophthalmologist and the founder of the Aravind Eye Foundation, a non-profit which supports the Aravind Eye Care System, which is a network of eye hospitals in Southern India.

Catherine Hirschman MEd, is a New York-based educator and consultant working towards her MBA at New York University's Leonard N. Stern School of Business with concentrations in Operations, Corporate Finance and Social Innovation and Impact.